Ready Reference for Microbes

Author

Kathy Brooks, RN, PhD, CPHQ

Aspiration of WBC
      <1000 = Ø infection
      thin non-clumped = Ø infection

gram - = red stain
gram + = purple stain

Printed in the United States of America.
Third Edition, June 2012
ISBN – 1-933013-53-2

All inquiries about the *Ready Reference for Microbes* or other APIC products and services may be addressed to:

APIC

1275 K Street, NW, Suite 1000
Washington, DC 20005-4006
Phone: 202-789-1890
Fax: 202-78-1899
Email: products@apic.org
Web: www.apic.org

Disclaimer
APIC provides information and services as a benefit to both APIC members and the general public. The material presented in this guide has been prepared in accordance with generally recognized infection prevention principles and practices and is for general information only. It is not intended to provide, or act as a substitute for, medical advice, and the user should consult a health care professional for matters regarding health and/or symptoms that may require medical attention. The guide and the information and materials contained therein are provided "AS IS", and APIC makes no representation or warranty of any kind, whether express or implied, including but not limited to, warranties of merchantability, noninfringement, or fitness, or concerning the accuracy, completeness, suitability, or utility of any information, apparatus, product, or process discussed in this resource, and assumes no liability therefore.

Table of Contents

Acknowledgements

Author

Kathy Brooks, RN, PhD, CPHQ
Chief, Quality Management (retired)
Overton Brooks VA Medical Center
Shreveport, LA

Contributor

Angela S. Hernandez, MPH, MT(ASCP)
Regional Safety and Quality Management Coordinator
Delta Pathology Group, LLC
Shreveport, LA

Reviewers

Lillian A. Burns, MT, MPH, CIC
Administrative Director Infection Control/Epidemiology
Staten Island University Hospital
Staten Island, NY

Carolyn Fiutem, MT(ASCP), CIC
Infection Prevention Officer
TriHealth
Cincinnati, OH

Marilyn Hanchett, RN, MA, CPHQ, CIC
Senior Director, Research and Clinical Innovation
APIC
Washington, DC

Deoine Reed, PhD, MSHCM, CIC
Infection Control Manager & Hospital/Healthcare Epidemiologist
Ochsner Clinic Foundation
New Orleans, LA

Thomas Weaver, DMD
Director, Professional Practice
APIC
Washington, DC

Production Team

Christina James
Project Management
Editorial Oversight

Thomas Weaver, DMD
Copy Editing

Sarah Vickers
Cover Design

Meredith McClay
Maryland Composition
Book Design & Layout

Preface

National and international attention remains sharply focused on healthcare associated infections. The global call for more effective prevention remains a priority for a diverse range of stakeholders. In fact, prevention efforts are increasingly important not only to those within the healthcare community, but to an expanding number of external audiences, including governmental, scientific, and consumer groups.

Infection prevention and control of potentially pathogenic organisms begins with a fundamental knowledge of the microbes, their categorization, and the risks they pose. This book is intended as a basic guide for infection preventionists (IPs) and other healthcare professionals who need quick access to essential information. References are provided at the end of each chapter for those who need more comprehensive information.

In this third edition of *Ready Reference for Microbes*, APIC has expanded the previous content first introduced in 2002. The core content on bacteria, fungi, parasites, viruses, common commensals and other normal flora, and bioterrorism agents has been updated and offers the most current web-based resources from authoritative sites. Color coding has been added to alert the reader to those microbes that are discussed in greater detail in the APIC Text.

In addition, the third edition includes a chapter on antimicrobial therapy and the importance of antimicrobial stewardship programs. A set of appendices that review popular topics, summarizing key facts and helpful reminders, is another new feature of this edition.

The resistance of microbes to existing pharmacologic therapies shows no sign of abating. As treatment options become more limited, the demand to prevent infection intensifies. The challenge for infection preventionists to respond to these growing demands also escalates. APIC offers this new edition of *Ready Reference for Microbes* to support IPs and others in healthcare in their ongoing efforts to control microbial risks and maximize patient safety across all practice settings.

Kathy Brooks, RN, PhD, CPHQ
Author

How To Use This Reference

Each chapter of the *Ready Reference for Microbes, 3rd edition* begins with an introduction and general information. Table formatting is used throughout the chapters with subheadings, general and specific notes provided where appropriate.

While many microbes are discussed in the APIC Text, rows highlighted in blue in this book indicate topics where substantive additional content can be cross-referenced in that comprehensive resource. Appendix A–G have been included to present quick facts about MRSA, *C. diff*, seasonal influenza (flu), antibiograms, contact precautions, common pathogens by site, and antimicrobial stewardship. This page provides the user with specific instructions on how to use the reference.

All chapters are formatted horizontally and are categorized by the following:

Chapter 1: Bacteria are listed in alphabetical order by genus.
Genus > Description > Name + (FKA) > Infections > Mode(s) of Transmission

Chapter 2: Fungi are listed in alphabetical order by genus.
Genus > Description > Name + (FKA) > Infections > Mode(s) of Transmission

Chapter 3: Parasites are listed in alphabetical order by genus.
Genus > Description > Name + (FKA) > Infections > Mode(s) of Transmission

Chapter 4: Viruses are listed in alphabetical order by the common name(s) and other associated names, if applicable.
Name + (AKA) > Description > Family/Genus > Infections and Syndromes > Transmission and Incubation

Chapter 5: Common commensal and other normal flora are listed in alphabetical order by body site.
Body Site > Normal Flora > Special Considerations of Specimen Collection

Chapter 6: Bioterrorism agents are listed in alphabetical order by microbes (bacteria, parasite, and virus).

Microbe > Disease Name > CDC Category > Issues related to Healthcare-associated Transmission > Treatment > Comments

Chapter 7: Antimicrobial therapy are listed by antimicrobial classes.

Class > Subclass > Representative Antimicrobial > Antimicrobial Activity

Chapter One

——

Bacteria

Bacterial agents are a part of our everyday life. Some bacteria are helpful and some can be harmful. Numerous strains and species of bacteria normally live benignly in and on the human body. Of the thousands of identified bacterial species, only a fraction is known to cause disease.

Growth

Bacteria are free-living, single cell organisms. Bacteria multiply through chromosomal replication and cellular division. A group of bacteria is referred to as a colony. The bacterial cell contains several components: DNA molecule, ribosomes, membrane, and cell wall. Some bacteria may have additional components such as an outer membrane, capsule, flagella, pili, or endospores.

Taxonomy

The classification of bacteria is based on morphological and chemical properties. The primary classification is the Gram-stain characteristics (Gram-positive vs. Gram-negative), the morphological features (cocci vs. bacilli {rod}), and oxygen utilization (aerobic vs. anaerobic). Other cell properties, which allow appropriate identification in the laboratory, are determined through additional tests such as catalase, coagulase, hemolysis on blood agar, sugar fermentation, and enzyme production. Bacteria are named according to genus and species. The correct format is genus (capitalized, italicized) and species (lowercase, italicized).

Examples:	genus	species
	Escherichia	*coli*
	Staphylococcus	*aureus*
	Pseudomonas	*aeruginosa*

Antibiotics and Vaccines

Antimicrobial agents work by killing the bacteria (bactericidal) or by preventing it from replicating (bacteriostatic). Examples of antimicrobial agents include penicillins that prevent cell wall synthesis, and rifampin and quinolones

Examples of Significant Bacterial Toxins

Bacteria	Toxin3	Results
Clostridium botulinum	botulinum toxin	interferes with neuromuscular transmission
Clostridium difficile	toxin A: enterotoxin toxin B: cytotoxin	create ulcers in the mucosa of the colon by causing mucosal inflammation, cell/tissue damage, and pseudomembrane formation
Clostridium tetani	tetanospasmin	interferes with nerve conduction at the neuromuscular junction
Corynebacterium diphtheria	diphtheria toxin	toxic to myocardial cells
MRSA	Panton-Valentine leukocidin (PVL) toxin	kills protective neutrophils and digests subcutaneous proteins that enhances rapid spread of infection
Staphylococcus aureus	Enterotoxins	stimulate GI peristalsis, activate complement, induce shock, e.g., toxic shock syndrome (TSS)
Vibrio cholera	cholera toxin	increases fluids secretion of the GI tract with profuse diarrhea and fluid and electrolyte loss

that inhibit protein or nucleic acid synthesis. (See Chapter Seven: Antimicrobial Therapy) Examples of vaccines that prevent bacterial infections are tetanus, pertussis (whooping cough), and pneumococcus.

Bioterrorism Agents

Microbes that are considered bioterrorism agents are denoted in the following manner: In the "Infections" column, the term **"bioterrorism agent"** is in bold letters. For special considerations regarding bioterrorism agents and category definitions, refer to Chapter Six: Bioterrorism Agents.

Toxins

Bacterial toxins have the capability of greatly increasing the virulence of pathogens. Toxins are classified as:

- Exotoxins, secreted by bacteria, mainly Gram-positive bacteria
  - Often heat inactivated
  - Neutralized by specific antibody
  - May possess enzymatic activity

For example, Panton-Valentine leukocidin (PVL) exotoxin enhances the virulence of community-acquired MRSA

- Endotoxins are surface components (complexes of bacterial proteins, lipids, and polysaccharides remaining firmly in the bacteria) of Gramnegative bacteria
  - Resist inactivation by heat
  - Partially neutralized by antibody
  - Interact with host systems, resulting in cascades of responses that induce, fever, swelling, vascular leaking, pain, and shock

Table

The following table will help guide the user through an understanding of bacteria. Note that the table:

- Lists the bacteria by Genus
- Provides a description of the bacteria as well as reservoirs or where normally found
- Lists the names and formerly known as names (**"Name + FKA"**) if applicable
- Lists the names and "also known as" (AKA) if applicable Describes infections and the mode(s) of transmission
- Describes infections and the mode(s) of transmission

Key terms:

- Aerobe/aerobic – requires oxygen to grow and survive
- Anaerobe/anaerobic – does not require oxygen to grow and is harmed by its presence
- Facultative anaerobe – can grow with or without oxygen
- Aerotolerant – does not use oxygen for growth but tolerates the presence of it

Genus	Description	Name + (FKA)	Infections	Mode(s) of Transmission
Achromobacter	Gram-negative rod; environmental flora	*A. xylosoxidans*	bite wounds, oral, head, neck, and miscellaneous soft tissue infections; bacteremia; meningitis; peritonitis; pneumonia; UTI; Healthcare Acquired Infection (HAI) from contaminated disinfectants	bites; water; soil
Acinetobacter	aerobic Gram-negative rod; widely distributed in nature; colonization of deployed Military to Iraq, referred to as "Iraqibacter".	*A. baumannii* *A. calcoaceticus* *A. haemolyticus* *A. johnsonii* *A. lwoffii*	HAI ventilator associated pneumonia; bacteremia; cause of infections following natural disasters; most frequently observed during warm seasons, respiratory, UTI, wounds (including catheter sites), and septicemia	direct, indirect, and environmental contact; endogenous
Actinomadura	aerobic Gram-positive rod; aerobic actinomycete; environmental (soil) flora	*A. madurae* *A. pelletieri*	localized infections result in mycetoma: chronic purulogranulomatous disease, begins as painless nodule at site of injury, produces sinus tracts, develops into destructive osteomyelitis; occasionally pulmonary or disseminated disease in immunocompromised individuals	puncture wound from a thorn or splinter
Actinomyces	anaerobic Gram-positive rod; anaerobic actinomycete; normal upper respiratory, vaginal and GI flora	*A. israelii*	actinomycosis: chronic suppurative granulomatous lesion, forms abscess and draining sinus; involved in pelvic inflammatory disease associated with intrauterine devices; polymicrobic infections	endogenous
Aerococcus	Gram-positive coccoid; environmental flora; occasionally found on skin	*A. urinae* *A. viridans*	peritonitis; lymphadenitis; endocarditis, bacteremia, and urinary tract infections	environmental contact
Aeromonas	Gram-negative rod; found in fresh, polluted, chlorinated, and/or brackish water, food	*A. caviae* *A. hydrophila* *A. sobria*	bacteremia; wound infections with indwelling catheter and drains, endocarditis, meningitis, pneumonia, osteomyelitis, peritonitis, conjunctivitis, thrombophlebitis, cholecystitis, gastroenteritis; and keratitis	contaminated foods (meats, produce, dairy) and potable water sources (fresh, polluted, marine); break in the skin

Genus	Characteristics	Species	Infection/Disease	Transmission
Afipia	Gram-negative rod; found in environment; normal oral flora of cat	*A. felis*	wound contamination; cat scratch fever	cat bites; environmental contact
Aggregatibacter	Gram-negative coccobacilli or small rod; oral cavity flora; *A. actinomycetem-comitans*: member of HACEK group	*A. actinomycetemcomitans* (*Actinobacillus actinomycetemcomitans*)	polymicrobic infections associated with endocarditis, periodontitis, and other focal infections including animal bites	animal bites; endogenous
	normal upper respiratory tract flora; member of HACEK group	*A. aphrophilus* (*Haemophilus aphrophilus*)		endogenous
Agrobacterium	See *Rhizobium*			
Alcaligenes	Gram-negative rod; environment (soil, water) flora	*A. faecalis* *A. piechaudii*	healthcare acquired septicemia; bacteremia; ocular and ear infections; pancreatic abscesses; pneumonia; and UTI	contact
Alloiococcus	aerobic Gram-positive cocci; widespread	*A. otitis*	middle ear infections; opportunistic pathogen in compromised host	endogenous
Anaplasma	zoonotic; Gram-negative obligate red cell intracellular bacteria; vector borne	*Anaplasma* spp.	Human granulocytic anaplasmosis (HGA)	tick bite
Arcanobacterium	Gram-positive rod; normal skin and pharynx flora	*A. haemolyticum* (*Corynebacterium haemolyticum*)	pharyngitis, peritonsillar abscess, wound infections, sepsis, osteomyelitis	endogenous
Arcobacter	curved Gram-negative rod; found in pigs, bulls, sheep, water, plant roots	*A. butzleri* *A. cryaerophilus* *A. nitrofigilis* *A. skirrowii*	*A. skirrowii* and *A. nitrofigilis* associated with bacteremia, endocarditis, peritonitis, and diarrhea	environmental contact
Arthrobacter	Gram-positive rod; found in soil	*A.cumminsii*	low pathogenicity; opportunistic in immuno-compromised patients	endogenous; environmental contact (soil)
Bacillus	zoonotic, Gram-positive spore forming aerobic rod; environmental flora; found in sheep, goats, and cattle	*B. anthracis*	characteristic blackened eschar; skin infection (malignant pustule), septicemia, pneumonia, "wool sorter's disease," enteritis, meningitis; **Category A bioterrorism agent**	enters through injured skin, mucous membranes; ingestion; inhalation; vaccine available to military

(continued)

Genus	Description	Name + (FKA)	Infections	Mode(s) of Transmission
	soil flora	B. cereus	food poisoning (toxin); opportunistic infections secondary to immuno-suppression; pneumonia; empyema; septicemia; meningitis; endocarditis; osteomyelitis; wound infections; fulminant liver failure; endophthalmitis; alcoholism; or neoplastic disease	environmental contact; ingestion of contaminated food
	soil flora	B. subtilis	opportunistic infections; pneumonia; septicemia; necrotic tumors; breast prosthesis; endocarditis; meningitis; surgical wounds; shunt infections	environmental contact
Bacteroides	enteric, anaerobic Gram-negative rod; normal flora GI tract	B. fragilis group B. ovatus B. thetaiotaomicron	polymicrobial infections; intra-abdominal closed abscesses from diverticulitis, ruptured appendix, or surgical procedures; bacteremia; lower respiratory infections; endocarditis; skin infections; gangrene; necrotizing fasciitis	endogenous; animal bites
Bartonella	Gram-negative rod; facultative intracellular parasite; vector borne (sand fly); human reservoir	B. bacilliformis	Carrion's disease; Oroya fever: fever, chills, headache, mental status changes with rapid and profound anemia; verruga peruana: nodular skin lesions	sand fly, ticks, fleas, mosquitos
	found in domestic cats	B. henselae	cat scratch disease, endocarditis, bacillary angiomatosis	cat bite, scratch; cat fleas; direct contact with cats; poor sanitation and personal hygiene
	found in small rodents; human reservoir	B. quintana	trench fever, endocarditis; opportunistic in immunocompromised	human body louse
Bifidobacterium	Gram-positive anaerobic rod; GI and upper respiratory flora	B. bifidum B. dentium	occasional pathogen in abscesses and pulmonary infections; perioperative wounds; dental caries; endodontic infections; polymicrobial infections	endogenous

Genus	Species	Description	Disease	Transmission
Bordetella	*B. bronchiseptica*	small aerobic Gram-negative coccobacilli; normal respiratory flora of dogs, cats, rabbits	pneumonitis, pertussis-like disease, wound infection	droplet; contact
	B. parapertussis	found in humans and lambs	pertussis-like disease	droplet
	B. pertussis	found in humans in disease state; colonize cilia of mammalian respiratory epithelial; can be carried by immune individuals	pertussis (whooping cough-uncontrollable, violent cough), pneumonia; impact unvaccinated children, adolescents/adults with waned immunity	droplet; immunization of infants with tetanus, diphtheria and pertussis vaccine; Chapter 4 - Use of Pertussis Vaccines in Outbreaks by Charles Virek, MD, MPH; http://www.cdc.gov (pertussis outbreak)
Borrelia	*B. burgdorferi*	spirochete, arthropod (tick) borne; reservoir: rodents	Lyme disease, a multi-system disease including neurologic and cardiac abnormalities, arthritis. TBRF=Tick-borne Relapsing Fever LB=Lyme Borrelioses	tick bite; vaccine available; serology testing ideal for identification
	B. recurrentis		relapsing fever LBRF=Louse-borne Relapsing Fever	human body louse vector; serology testing ideal for identification
Branhamella		See *Moraxella*		
Brucella	*B. abortus* *B. canis* *B. melitensis* *B. suis*	zoonotic, aerobic Gram-negative coccobacilli; found in cattle and goats (*B. abortus*); dogs (*B. canis*); sheep (*B. melitensis*); pigs (*B. suis*)	acute brucellosis, undulant fever, "Malta fever"; fever, chills, TB-like symptoms; arthritis, osteomyelitis, epididymitis, endocarditis, hepatitis, granulomatous disease, nodular lung and ocular lesions; **Category B bioterrorism agent**	breaks in skin and mucous membrane; inhalation; ingestion of contaminated meat or dairy products
Burkholderia	*B. cepacia* (*Pseudomonas cepacia*)	aerobic Gram-negative rod; found in water, soil and plants (fruits & vegetables); may colonize respiratory tract of cystic fibrosis patients	bacteremia, peritonitis, septic arthritis, respiratory and urinary tract infections, often healthcare acquired due to contaminated equipment	contaminated equipment, indwelling catheters, disinfectants (i.e., povidone iodine)

(continued)

Genus	Description	Name + (FKA)	Infections	Mode(s) of Transmission
	zoonotic, aerobic Gram-negative rod; primarily a disease of horses, mules, and donkeys	B. mallei	Glanders: pneumonia, pulmonary abscesses, septicemia; acute disease: localized infection with ulceration at laceration or abrasion site; chronic disease: multiple abscesses of liver, spleen, skin, or muscles; **Category B bioterrorism agent**	direct skin or mucous membrane contact with infected animal tissues; rare in humans; occurs primarily in veterinarians, animal caretakers, abattoir workers, and laboratory personnel
	occurs in tropical/subtropical regions (soil, streams, rice paddies), may be dormant for decades	B. pseudomallei (Pseudomonas pseudomallei)	melioidosis, ranges from asymptomatic to fulminant sepsis; liver, lung, spleen, skin, soft tissue, joints, and bone abscesses; **Category B bioterrorism agent**	travel related illness; inhalation; contact of cut skin with contaminated soil or water
Campylobacter	enteric, Gram-negative V& S-shaped rod; found in pigs, poultry, birds, cats, dogs	C. coli, C. fetus, C. jejuni	gastroenteritis, sepsis, meningitis, abscesses, UTI, peritonitis, and pancreatitis	contact with contaminated feces, soil, water, food; sexually transmitted (gay bowel syndrome)
Capnocytophaga	facultative anaerobic Gram-negative rod; found in oral cavity and subgingival surfaces	C. gingivalis, C. ochracea, C. sputigena	septicemia; endocarditis; peritonitis; keritinis; meningitis; ; and periodontal diseases	bite wounds; contact with bleeding gums or abscesses in oral cavity
Cardiobacterium	facultative anaerobic Gram-negative rod; normal upper respiratory tract flora; C. hominis: member of HACEK group	C. hominis	endocarditis	endogenous
Chlamydia	intracellular parasite, Gram-negative cocci; reservoir humans	C. trachomatis	endemic trachoma, urethritis, cervicitis, proctitis, epididymitis, endometriosis, salpingitis, perihepatitis, PID (pelvic inflammatory disease), LGV (lymphogranuloma venereum); pneumonia	contact with contaminated conjunctiva, sputum, feces; sexual transmission
Chlamydophila	intracellular parasite, Gram-negative cocci; found in humans	C. pneumoniae	pneumonia; bronchitis; pharyngitis; and sinusitis	airborne
	reservoir: psittacine birds	C. psittaci (Chlamydia psittaci)	systemic infections; psittacosis; **Category B bioterrorism agent**	inhalation of bird feces particles

Chromobacterium	facultative anaerobe Gram-negative coccobacillus; found in soil and water of tropical/subtropical regions	*C. violaceum*	sepsis, skin lesions, liver abscesses, puncture and contaminated wounds	contact with contaminated soil, water, wounds, blood
Chryseobacterium	Gram-negative rod; found in soil, plants, water, and food; found in hospital water sources (sinks, faucets, hemodialysis systems)	*C. indologenes*	infraorbital drain, aortic valve infections, dialysis fluid, sepsis, neonatal meningitis, pneumonia	contact with blood, CSF, respiratory secretions; indwelling devices
Citrobacter	enteric, Gram-negative rod; normal GI tract flora	*C. amalonaticus* *C. diversus* *C. freundii* *C. koseri*	wounds, UTI, sepsis, meningitis; brain abscesses	contact with feces, blood, urine, respiratory secretions, wounds
Clostridium	enteric, anaerobic spore-containing Gram-positive rod; soil saprophytes; marine sediment	*C. botulinum*	botulism, food poisoning; botulinum toxin; **Category A bioterrorism agent**	contact with soil, food (e.g., home canned vegetables, fresh honey)
	reservoir: intestinal tract and environmental	*C. difficile*	pseudomembranous colitis; antibiotic associated disease; hypervirulent strain toxins a and b; toxic megacolon and large bowel rupture	fecal-oral; healthcare acquired diarrheal disease
	reservoir: soil and GI tract	*C. perfringens*	wounds, intra-abdominal and brain abscesses, sepsis; Epsilon toxin = **Category B bioterrorism agent**	environmental contact; endogenous
	soil, feces, sewerage, and marine sediments	*C. septicum*	bacteremia, skin and soft tissue infections; non-traumatic gas gangrene	environmental contact; endogenous
	reservoir: soil	*C. tetani*	tetanus, gas gangrene, tetanospasm	contact with soil; immunity induced by tetanus toxoid vaccine
Coagulase-negative *Staphylococcus*	Gram-positive cocci; normal skin and mucous membranes flora; approximately 40 species and subspecies	See *Staphylococcus epidermidis*	prosthetic orthopedic and vascular devices; peritonitis, endocarditis, sepsis, subcutaneous wounds, UTI	indwelling catheters and shunts; contact with blood, urine, wounds, body fluids; endogenous

(continued)

Genus	Description	Name + (FKA)	Infections	Mode(s) of Transmission
Corynebacterium	Gram-positive rod; coryneform bacteria; found in soil, water, plants, food products, normal skin and mucosal flora	*C. diphtheriae* - inhabits nasopharynx only in carrier state *C. minutissimum* *C. pseudodiphbheriticum* *C. striatum* *C. urealyticum* *C. xerosis*	diphtheria, pharyngitis, cutaneous wounds, conjunctivitis, endocarditis, pneumonia, UTI; *C. diphtheriae* = diphtheria toxin	contact with respiratory secretions and droplets, cutaneous lesions, or contaminated objects
Coxiella	zoonotic; obligate intracellular Gram-negative rod; reservoir: urine, feces of cattle, sheep, goats	*C. burnetti*	etiologic agent of Q fever: febrile illness, pneumonia, endocarditis, hepatitis, encephalitis, osteomyelitis; **Category B bioterrorism agent**	inhalation of infectious aerosols; inhalation of 1 organism will yield disease in 50% of the population exposed
Diphtheroids	See *Corynebacterium*			
Edwardsiella	enteric, facultative anaerobic Gram-negative rod; found in cold-blooded animals (fish and reptiles) and their environment	*E. tarda*	opportunistic bacteremia and wound infections; *Salmonella*-like enteritis, more often in young children and elderly, mainly in tropical and subtropical climates	fecal-oral
Ehrlichia	zoonotic; Gram-negative obligate intracellular bacteria	*E. chaffeensis*	spectrum of disease ranges from subclinical infection/mild illness to severe life threatening/fatal disease; non-specific symptoms: fever, headache, anorexia, nausea, myalgia and vomiting; can be confused with Rocky Mountain spotted fever but usually lacks presence of rash	no evidence of person to person transmission; tick bites
	natural reservoir: white tailed deer and domestic dogs	*E. ewingii*	human monocytotropic ehrlichiosis (HME); most cases identified in South Central and South Eastern U.S.	lone star tick bite

Genus	Characteristics	Species	Diseases/Manifestations	Transmission
Eikenella	facultative anaerobic Gram-negative rod; normal flora oral and GI tract; *E. corrodens*: member of HACEK group	*E. corrodens* (CDC group HB-1)	periodontitis, pleuropulmonary, surgical site infections, meningitis, endocarditis; joint wounds and septicemia; cellulitis in drug addicts from direct inoculation after oral contamination of needle paraphernalia (licking needle clean instead of sterilizing)	trauma, especially after fights or bites; syringes; endogenous
Elizabethkingia	Gram-negative rod; environment: soil, water, plants, and food stuffs	*E. meningoseptica* (*Flavobacterium meningosepticum*)	meningitis, healthcare acquired mini-epidemics, endocarditis, retroperitoneal hematoma, adult septicemia; respiratory colonization and infection following aerosol treatment; Cystic Fibrosis airway infections; community-acquired osteomyelitis, pneumonia, and septicemia	environmental contact
Enterobacter	enteric, Gram-negative, facultative anaerobic rod; widespread throughout the environment	*E. asburiae*, *E. aerogenes*, *E. cloacae*, *E. gergoviae*, *E. sakazakii*	UTI, wound, bloodstream infections and pneumonia; opportunistic infections in patients (diabetic, neutropenic) exposed frequently to antibiotics, invasive procedures, and indwelling catheters	unwashed hands; contaminated medical devices and instrumentation; commonly consumed in food and water; endogenous
Enterococcus	enteric, Gram-positive cocci, pairs or chains; facultative anaerobic; normal GI and female genital tract flora; endogenous in soil, food, water, and plants; opportunistic agents	*E. faecalis*, *E. faecium*, *E. casseliflavus*, *E. gallinarum*, *E. raffinosus* (Lancefield group D *Streptococcus*)	UTI, bloodstream, wound infections, endocarditis, intra-abdominal/pelvic wounds; *faecalis* and *faecium* have acquired resistance to Vancomycin (VRE); *casseliflavus*, *gallinarum*, and *raffinosus* have intrinsic (naturally occurring) resistance to Vancomycin; surgical site infections	contact; endogenous; HAI-VRE
Erysipelothrix	zoonotic; facultative anaerobic Gram-positive rod; found in mammals, birds, fish, contaminated water, and soil; reservoir: swine	*E. rhusiopathiae*	erysipeloid: localized skin infection or cellulitis on hands and fingers, mild and self-limiting with formation of characteristic edematous lesion, lasting about 1 month; sepsis and endocarditis in persons with heart valve disease, alcoholism, or other predisposing conditions; regional lymphangitis	handling infected animals or animal products; occupational disease in veterinarians, butchers, and fish handlers

(continued)

Genus	Description	Name + (FKA)	Infections	Mode(s) of Transmission
Escherichia	enteric, Gram-negative, facultative anaerobic rod; ubiquitous in humans; presence in water considered indication of fecal contamination; reservoir: GI and female GU tracts; opportunistic pathogen	E. coli E. coli 0157: H7 E. coli 0157:NM	UTI, septicemia, and neonatal meningitis; 5 major GI infections: 1) enteropathogenic—infantile diarrhea, a cause of chronic diarrhea; 2) enterotoxigenic—"travelers" diarrhea, self limiting illness; 3) enteroinvasive - occurs most commonly in children in developing countries; 4) enterohemorrhagic (serotype 0157:H7)—associated with hemorrhagic diarrhea, colitis, and hemolytic uremic syndrome (HUS); shigatoxin (verotoxin); 5) enteroaggregative - pediatric diarrhea in less developed countries; persistent diarrhea in HIV patients; E. coli 0157:H7 = **Category B bioterrorism agent**	fecal-oral route; E. coli 0157:H7: ingestion of contaminated inadequately cooked beef; raw milk, fruits and vegetables contaminated with ruminant feces; person to person contact; waterborne transmission of neonatal infections through maternal genital tract
Eubacterium	anaerobic Gram-positive rod; normal flora upper respiratory, GI tract, vagina	E. brachy E. infirmum E. minutum E. nodatum	intrauterine device related infections and pelvic inflammatory disease (PID); chronic periodontal disease; opportunistic infections involving head, neck, and lungs; common in infections associated with surgery, malignancy, immunodeficiency, diabetes, dental extraction, broad-spectrum antibiotics, and presence of a foreign body; bite wounds; upper respiratory infections; and necrotizing soft tissue infections	bites; endogenous; environmental contact
Flavobacterium	See Elizabethkingia			
Francisella	zoonotic, fastidious facultative intracellular aerobic Gram-negative coccobacilli; vector borne; water, grasslands, haystacks	F. tularensis	Ohara's disease; Rabbit fever; tularemia: ulceroglandular form seen on upper extremities from exposure to infected mammals; lesions on lower extremities, head and back from bite of blood-sucking arthropod (tick, deer fly, or mosquito); **Category A bioterrorism agent**	infected wild animals; infected arthropod bite; inhalation; water; Note: special handling in microbiology labs necessary if isolated from clinical culture

Genus	Description	Species	Infections	Transmission
Fusobacterium	anaerobic Gram-negative pleomorphic organism; normal flora GI and upper respiratory tracts	*F. mortiferum* *F. naviforme* *F. necrophorum* *F. nucleatum* *F. periodonticum*	oral, dental, and bite infections; severe pharyngotonsillitis, peritonsillar abscesses, neck space infections, jugular vein septic thrombophlebitis, intra-abdominal infections, bacteremia, multiple metastatic abscesses (lungs, pleural space, liver, large joints); polymicrobic infections	endogenous; persists in mud, water, and decaying animal carcasses
Gardnerella	anaerobic gram variable rod or coccobacilli; natural habitat: vagina of reproductive age women; colonizes distal urethra of males	*G. vaginalis*	postpartum sepsis; bacterial vaginosis, UTI, bacteremia associated with postpartum endometriosis, chorioamnionitis, septic abortion, and infection after C-section	endogenous; sexually transmitted
Gemella	aerobic Gram-positive cocci; normal oral and upper respiratory tract flora	*G. haemolysans*	ocular infections; brain abscesses; endocarditis, meningitis, wounds, and abscesses; total knee replacement	endogenous
		G. morbillorum	septic shock; brain abscesses; osteomyelitis; septic arthritis; peritonitis; endocarditis; empyema and lung abscess; blood; respiratory, genitourinary, wounds and abscesses	endogenous
Gordonia	aerobic Gram-positive, partially pleomorphic, acid-fast non-motile rod; aerobic actinomycete; opportunistic	*G. bronchialis* *G. otitidis* *G. rubripertincta* *G. sputi* *G. terrae* (*Rhodococcus*)	catheter-related and medical device-related infections; cutaneous infections, bacteremia, and brain abscesses; primarily in immuno-compromised	environmental contact
HACEK group	an acronym consisting of the first initial of each genus; all are opportunistic and require an immuno-compromised host; normal flora of the oral cavity	*Haemophilus* spp. *Aggregatibacter aphrophilus* *Cardiobacterium hominis* *Eikenella corrodens* *Kingella kingae*	endocarditis with predilection for attachment to heart valves (usually damaged or prosthetic)	endogenous
Haemophilus	Gram-negative coccobacilli; normal flora of upper respiratory tract, colonizers of GI and urogenital tracts			

(continued)

Genus	Description	Name + (FKA)	Infections	Mode(s) of Transmission
	found in urogenital tract only during infections	*H. ducreyi* (*Ducrey's bacillus*)	chancroid (soft chancre), an acute ulcerative disease involves genitalia; suppurative, enlarged, draining inguinal lymph nodes (buboes) are common	sexually transmitted disease
	normal upper respiratory tract flora	*H. influenzae*	meningitis, orbital cellulitis, conjunctivitis, otitis media, acute maxillary sinusitis, epiglottis, and bacteremia; usually found in pediatric population	direct contact; inhalation of droplets; endogenous; *H. influenzae* type B (HIB) conjugated vaccine available prevents meningitis in children >2 months of age
	normal upper respiratory tract flora	*H. influenzae biotype III*	Brazilian purpuric fever	direct contact; inhalation of droplets; endogenous
	normal flora upper respiratory tract	*H. aegyptius* (*H. aegyptius Koch-Weeks bacillus*)	acute contagious conjunctivitis ("pink eye")	contact with conjunctiva or upper respiratory tract discharges, contaminated fingers, clothing, other articles: shared eye makeup applicators, multi-dose eye medications, inadequately sterilized instruments (e.g., tonometers)
	normal upper respiratory tract flora	*H. parainfluenzae*	acute otitis media; acute sinusitis; chronic bronchitis; endocarditis	endogenous
Hafnia	enteric, Gram-negative rod; found in the GI tract and environment (surface water, sewage, food (meat), and dairy products)	*H. alvei* (*Enterobacter hafniae*)	opportunistic infections and gastroenteritis; wound and abscess infections	environmental contact; endogenous
Helicobacter	Gram-negative rod; found in the gastric mucosa	*H. pylori* (*Campylobacter pylori*)	duodenal ulcers and chronic active gastritis; chronic infections possible risk factor for gastric carcinoma; acute upper gastrointestinal illness with nausea, vomiting, and abdominal pain	fecal-oral and oral-oral; person-to-person via improperly cleaned endoscopes

	Description	Species	Diseases/Infections	Transmission
	found in GI tract	*H. cinaedi* *H. fennelliae*	gastroenteritis; suspected agent of septicemia; particularly in immunocompromised individuals	fecal-oral
Kingella	aerobic Gram-negative coccobacillus; normal upper respiratory and GU tract flora; *K. kingae*: member of HACEK group	*K. kingae* *K. denitrificans* *K. oralis*	endocarditis, infections of the bone, joints, tendons, osteomyelitis; occasionally bacteremia	hematogenous, possibly trauma of the oral-pharyngeal mucosa
Klebsiella	enteric, aerobic Gram-negative rod; normal flora intestinal genital tracts	*K. granulomatis* (*Calymmatobacterium granulomatis*) *K. oxytoca* *K. pneumoniae*	lobar pneumonia, lung abscess, UTI, bacteremia, enteritis and meningitis (in infants), wound infections, rhinoscleroma; STD-granuloma inguinale or donovanosis	contact with ulcerative genital lesions; endogenous
Klayvera	Gram-negative, facultative anaerobic rod; found in sputum, urine, stool, blood, water, sewage, soil, food, and animals	*K. ascorbata* (Enteric group 8) *K. cryocrescens*	bacteremia, respiratory and soft tissue infections, pyelonephritis, opportunistic infections	contact; endogenous
Lactobacillus	anaerobic Gram-positive, micro-aerophillic facultative coccobacilli rod; normal flora mouth, GI tract and female GU tract	*L. acidophilus*	polymicrobic infections; generally nonpathogenic; rarely associated with pulmonary infections, chorioamnionitis, endocarditis, neonatal meningitis, and bacteremia; endodontic infections; peritonitis; pelvic inflammatory disease (PID)	contact; endogenous; bite wounds
Lactococcus	Gram-positive cocci; found in foods and vegetation	*L. garvieae* *L. lactis* (Lancefield group N *Streptococci*)	endocarditis, urinary tract infections, bacteremia	contact; endogenous
Legionella	Gram-negative rod; found in lakes, rivers, streams, thermally heated bodies of water, contaminated air-conditioning systems, shower heads, cooling towers, hot water tanks, humidifiers, respiratory therapy equipment, and whirlpools	*L. pneumophila*	Legionnaires' disease: high fever and severe pneumonia, with or without abscess; Pontiac fever: flu-like illness, headache, muscle aches, fatigue, and chills	inhalation of aerosolized organisms from environmental sources or aspiration of organisms; no evidence of person-to-person transmission

(continued)

Genus	Description	Name + (FKA)	Infections	Mode(s) of Transmission
Leptospira	zoonotic, aerobic Gram-negative spirochete; concentrated in urine of wild and domesticated animals (rats, swine, cattle, dogs, and raccoons); ubiquitous organism	L. interrogans	bacteremia; nephritis; hepatitis; skin, muscle, and eye lesions; meningitis; and pulmonary infections	food borne; contact (breaks in the skin or mucous membranes) with urine of infected animals; possibly through aerosolized contaminated fluids
Leuconostoc	Gram-positive cocci; found in plants, vegetables, dairy	L. mesenteroides	pulmonary infections, cerebral spinal fluid, peritoneal dialysate fluid, bacteremia (esp. neonates), wounds, abdominal abscesses, tracheostomy sites, fistulas, odontogenic, and breast abscesses	contact
Listeria	Gram-positive rod; found in soil and vegetable matter; may colonize GI tract	L. monocytogenes serotypes Ia, Ib, and IVb	perinatal listeriosis (may be intrauterine infection) or meningitis; adults may develop meningoencephalitis, bacteremia, endocarditis, and rarely, focal infections	food borne (raw milk, soft cheeses, vegetables, and ready-to-eat meats); perinatal transmission; contact; contaminated equipment
Micrococcus	aerobic Gram-positive cocci; coagulase-negative and can be mistaken for Coagulase-negative Staphylococci; widely distributed in nature; normal flora of skin, mucosa and oropharynx		nonpathogenic; rarely implicated in infections, low virulence	environmental contact; endogenous
Moraxella	aerobic Gram-negative diplo-bacilli; normal flora of mucosal surfaces, respiratory tract, naso-pharynx, conjunctiva flora	M. catarrhalis (Branhamella cattarhalis) M. nonliquefaciens M. canis	eye infections, bacteremia, endocarditis, septic arthritis, otitis media, sinusitis and pneumonia; dog bite wounds	droplet; patient care equipment; dog bites; endogenous
Morganella	enteric, facultative anaerobic Gram-negative rod; normal GI tract flora; environment	M. morganii	UTI, wounds, bacteremia, meningitis and other various infections	endogenous; person-to-person spread, especially in hospitalized patients
MRSA (Methicillin-Resistant Staphylococcus aureus)	See Staphylococcus aureus		Penton-Valentine leukocidin (PVL) toxin increases virulence of MRSA	

Myobacterium	acid-fast bacilli; free-living in diseased tissue of humans and animals		
M. africanum	slow growing; found in diseased tissue of humans and animals	tuberculosis in tropical Africa; common to east and west Africa; has been reported from other continents including United States	airborne
M. bovis	slow growing; found in animals (cattle, goats, pigs, dogs, deer)	tuberculosis-like illness	ingestion of contaminated milk from infected cows
M. bovis BCG	slow growing; vaccine-induced disease	systemic BCG (Bacillus Calmett-Guerin) infection	vaccine induced
M. caprae		tuberculosis-like illness	contact with contaminate materials
M. leprae	slow growing; does not grow in culture media, must be cultured in armadillos	Hansen's disease: tuberculoid leprosy involving skin, mucous membranes, and nerve tissue	person to person; prolonged contact with infected host, organism is shed from the infected patient's nose; direct through penetrating wounds or mucous membranes; handling of the nine-banded armadillo native to the southern United States.
M. tuberculosis complex –includes the following species: M. tuberculosis M. bovis M. bovis BCG M. africanum M. caprae M. microti M. canettii	slow growing; found in diseased tissue of humans	pulmonary tuberculosis; can involve genito-urinary tract, lymph nodes, central nervous system, bones, pericardium, and other body sites	airborne droplets

(continued)

Genus	Description	Name + (FKA)	Infections	Mode(s) of Transmission
		Multidrug-resistant *M. tuberculosis* [MDR-TB]	organism has resistance to at least isoniazid and rifampicin; result in high fatality rates and transmission to individuals with direct contact **Category C bioterrorism agent**	airborne droplets; direct contact with infected individuals
		Extensively drug resistant *M. tuberculosis* (XDR-TB)	organism has resistance to at least isoniazid and rifampicin, and to any fluoroquinolone and resistance to at least one of the following: amikacin, kanamycin, or capreomycin; result in high fatality rates and transmission to individuals with direct contact	airborne droplets; direct contact with infected individuals
MOTT (*Mycobacteria Other Than Tuberculosis*)	found in soil, water, plants, animals, and water systems rapid growing; found in tap water, water, and soil		opportunistic infections in immunocompromised; pulmonary infections with pre-existing pulmonary disease; disseminated disease involves bone marrow, lungs, liver, lymph nodes	environmental contact; not transmitted between humans
	rapid growing; found in soil, water, plants, animals, indoor water systems, hot tubs, and pools	*M. abscessus*	disseminated disease in immunocompromised; skin, soft tissue, pulmonary, post-operative infections (sternal and mammoplasty); bacteremia associated with hemodialysis equipment	environmental contact, tap water; not transmitted between humans
	nonchromogen; slow growing; found in water and soil	*M. avium complex* (MAC) aka *M. avium-intracellulare*	opportunistic infections in AIDS: disseminated wasting disease characterized by fever, weight loss, hepatosplenomegaly, anemia; localized lymphadenitis in the submandibular, submaxillary, and periauricular lymph nodes in children; most common environmental nontuberculosis mycobacterium (NTM) causing disease	environmental contact; tap water; not transmitted between humans
	rapid growing; found in water, soil, and dust	*M. chelonae*	skin, soft tissue, post-operative wound infections, keratitis	environmental contact, tap water; not transmitted between humans

Growth characteristics	Species	Disease	Transmission
rapid growing; found in tap water, soil, and dust	M. fortuitum	nonpathogenic; skin abscess at site of trauma; can cause infections in individuals that are patrons of nail salons	environmental contact, tap water; not transmitted between humans
nonchromogen; slow growing; found in environment; reservoir: pet birds and dogs	M. genavense	disseminated wasting disease in AIDS patients	environmental contact; not transmitted between humans
scotochromogen; slow growing; found in tap water, water, and soil	M. gordonae	nonpathogenic	environmental contact; not transmitted between humans
photochromogen; slow growing; found in water and soil	M. kansasii	pulmonary disease	environmental contact; not transmitted between humans
nonchromogen; slow growing; found in humans and armadillos; majority of cases from England, Wales, Sweden	M. malmoense	chronic pulmonary infections in persons with pre-existing disease; cervical lymphadenitis in children; less common infections of skin or bursa	environmental contact; not transmitted between humans
photochromogen; slow growing; found in some fish; acquired from fish tanks	M. marinum	fish tank granuloma; cutaneous disease and skin lesions; severe complications result in tenosynovitis, arthritis, bursitis, and osteomyelitis	contaminated fresh water or salt-water from infected fish and other marine life, enters by small breaks in skin; usually associated with aquatic activity and fishing; not transmitted between humans
scotochromogen; slow growing; found in water, soil, raw milk, dairy products	M. scrofulaceum	cervical adenitis in children; adenitis in general	raw milk, soil, water, dairy products; not transmitted between humans
scotochromogen; slow growing; found in water and soil	M. szulgai	nonpathogenic; opportunistic pulmonary, skin, lymph node, and joint infections seen in immunocompromised	environmental contact; not transmitted between humans
slow growing; occurs in tropical or temperate climates	M. ulcerans	Buruli or Bairnsdale ulcer, indolent cutaneous and subcutaneous infections; mycolactone (cytotoxin) causes necrosis	environmental contact, tropical wetlands, mud; not transmitted between humans

(continued)

Genus	Description	Name + (FKA)	Infections	Mode(s) of Transmission
	scotochromogen; slow growing; found in water	*M. xenopi*	pulmonary infections in adults; extrapulmonary infections (bone, lymph node, sinus tract) and disseminated disease; HAI and pseudoinfection from water storage tanks	water, especially hot water taps in hospitals via aerosols; not transmitted between humans
Mycoplasma	aerobic pleomorphic Gram-negative cell-wall defective bacteria; less than 1 micron in size			droplet; direct contact
	hominis group; found in genital tract	*M. hominis* *M. genitalium*	neonatal systemic infections, meningitis, abscess, and pneumonia; invasive disease in immunosuppressed patients: bacteremia, abscesses, wound infections, peritonitis; urogenital tract infections, prostatitis, PID, bacterial vaginosis, amnionitis, urethritis	direct contact: sexual, cervical, and vaginal contact
	pneumonia group; found in respiratory tract	*M. pneumoniae*	upper respiratory tract infections in children with mild nonspecific symptoms; lower respiratory tract infections in adults with nonproductive cough, fever, malaise	droplet; direct contact
Neisseria	Gram-negative diplococci; normal upper respiratory tract flora	*N. cinerea* *N. elongata* *N. mucosa* *N. sicca*	opportunistic infections in immunocompromised, localized to respiratory tract, rarely disseminated	endogenous
	Gram-negative intracellular diplococci; sexually transmitted disease	*N. gonorrhoeae* aka gonococcus	gonorrhea; proctitis, vulvovaginitis, urethritis, cervicitis, salpingitis, prostatitis, stomatitis, conjunctivitis, pharyngitis, epididymitis, bartholinitis, skin lesions, tenosynovitis, septicemia, endocarditis, and newborn ophthalmitis; pharyngitis, tonsilitis, bacteremic dissemination, and vasculitic skin lesions	person-to-person via sexual contact; infected mother to baby at birth

	Characteristics	Species	Disease/Manifestations	Transmission
	colonizes oropharyngeal and nasopharyngeal mucous membranes; asymptomatic carriers may serve as source of later dissemination	*N. meningitidis* aka meningococcus	meningitis, death may occur quickly due to endotoxin shock or focal cerebral involvement; purpuric skin lesions; hemorrhage and necrosis of the adrenal glands (Waterhouse-Friderichsen syndrome); bacteremia, pneumonia, pericarditis, arthritis	respiratory droplets; group A, C, Y, and W135 vaccines available
Neorickettsia	intracellular parasite of monocytes and macrophages; reservoir: fish	*N. sennetsu (Ehrlichia sennetsu)*	Glandular fever or Sennetsu fever; self-limited febrile illness with chills, headache, malaise, sore throat, anorexia and generalized lymphadenopathy (similar to infectious mononucleosis); identified in Japan; neorickettsiosis	consumption of raw fish containing trematodes
Nocardia	long thin Gram-positive beaded bacilli with branching filaments; aerobic actinomycete; partial acid-fast positivie; found in soil and water	*N. asteroides* *N. brasiliensis*	actinomycotic mycetoma; nocardiosis, mycetoma, lung, brain, skin, and soft tissue infections	traumatic inoculation or inhalation
Orientia	obligate intracellular Gram-negative cocco-bacilli; vector borne; found in Southeast Asia, South Pacific; reservoir: rodents; vector borne	*O. tsutsugamushi (Rickettsia tsutsugamushi)*	scrub typhus (*tsutsugamushi* fever) clinically resembles epidemic typhus; maculopapular rash; site of bite develops black eschar; interstitial pneumonia and lymphadenitis	chigger bites; trombiculid mites
Paenibacillus	facultative anaerobic Gram-positive spore forming rod; widely distributed in nature; transient colonizer of skin, GI, and respiratory tracts	*P. alvei (Bacillus alvei)*	endophthalmitis; meningitis, prosthetic hip, and wound infections	environmental contact
		P. macerans	opportunistic infections in neutropenic persons; wound infections; brain abscesses; catheter-associated infection bacteremia	traumatic introduction into sterile site; exposure to contaminated medical equipment

(continued)

Genus	Description	Name + (FKA)	Infections	Mode(s) of Transmission
Pantoea	enteric, aerobic Gram-negative bacilli; found in the environment; opportunistic pathogen in immunocompromised	*P. agglomerans (Enterobacter agglomerans)*	soft tissue infections; septic arthritis; osteomyelitis; penetrating trauma by objects from contamination of soil or vegetative	HAI- contaminated intravenous fluid and parenteral nutrition
Pasteurella	facultative anaerobic, small Gram-negative coccobacilli or rod; found in nasopharynx and GI tracts of wild and domestic animals and respiratory flora of animal handlers	*P. canis* *P. dagmatis* *P. multocida* *P. stomatis*	focal soft tissue infections following bite or scratch; chronic respiratory infections in persons with preexisting chronic lung disease and heavy exposure to animals; bacteremia with metastatic abscess formation in persons with no history of animal exposure; sinusitus and bronchitis	animal (dog or cat) bite or scratch
Pediococcus	facultative anaerobic Gram-positive cocci; found in foods and vegetation; colonize GI tract of immunocompromised	*P. acidilactici*	usually only capable of causing infections in severely compromised; whenever encountered in clinical specimens, first consider as probable contaminant; bacteremia and hepatic abscesses	environmental contact; endogenous
Peptococcus	Gram-positive anaerobic cocci; present in vagina of 20-30% of pregnant women	*P. niger*	nonpathogenic	endogenous
Peptostreptococcus	anaerobic Gram-positive coccus; normal flora of skin, oropharynx, respiratory, GI, and GU tracts	*P. anaerobius* *P. asaccharolyticus* *P. magnus* *P. micros* *P. prevotii* *P. tetradius*	cutaneous, respiratory, oral or female pelvic infections: tubo-ovarian abscesses, septic abortions, bacteremia, amnionitis and chorioamnionitis; periodontitis, chronic otitis media, chronic sinusitis, purulent nasopharyngitis, brain abscess, endocarditis, pneumonitis, lung abscess, empyema, necrotizing pneumonia; intestinal perforation or cancer may lead to peritonitis with mixed infections, liver abscess	endogenous

Genus	Description	Species	Disease/Infection	Transmission
Plesiomonas	facultative anaerobic Gram-negative rod; found in fresh water in warmer climates	*P. shigelloides*	gastroenteritis; septicemia in compromised adults, and infants experiencing complicated delivery	ingestion of contaminated water or seafood; exposure to cold-blooded animals, such as amphibia and reptiles
Porphyromonas	anaerobic Gram-negative coccobacilli; normal flora upper respiratory and GI tracts	*P. asaccharolytica* *P. catoniae* *P. gingivalis* *P. levii*	oral, dental, bite infections, head, neck, lower respiratory and urogenital tract infections	endogenous
		P. bennonis (new species)	perirectal, buttock, and wound infections	endogenous
Prevotella	anaerobic Gram-negative coccobacilli; normal flora of oral, upper respiratory, GI, and GU tracts	*P. bivia* *P. disiens*	female genital tract infections and less frequently oral infections	endogenous
		P. buccae *P. oris*	variety of oral, pleuropulmonary, human bite wounds and other infections	human bites; endogenous
		P. dentalis (Hallella seregens)	infected root canals, periodontal pockets, mandibular and gum abscesses, and sialadenitis	endogenous
		P. melaninogenica	head, neck, pleuropulmonary infections, and human bite wounds	endogenous
Propionibacterium	anaerobic and aerotolerant diphtheroid-like Gram-positive rod; normal flora of skin, oral cavity, respiratory tract, and vagina	*P. acnes* *P. propionicum*	acne; most common anaerobic blood culture contaminant; linked to surgical procedures or foreign bodies; uveitis, endophthalmitis, bone, joints, Central Nervous System (CNS) infections; endocarditis; associated with SAPHO syndrome (synovitis, acne, pustulosis, hyperostosis, and osteomyelitis); dog and cat bite wounds; oral cavity infections; and eye infections	endogenous; cat and dog bites
Proteus	enteric, facultative anaerobic Gram-negative rod; normal gastrointestinal flora	*P. mirabilis* *P. penneri* *P. vulgaris*	wide variety of healthcare acquired infections of respiratory tract, urinary tract, blood, and several other normally sterile sites; most frequently in seriously debilitated patients	endogenous; person to person

(continued)

Genus	Description	Name + (FKA)	Infections	Mode(s) of Transmission
Providencia	aerobic and facultative anaerobic enteric, coccobacilli or straight rod; normal gastrointestinal flora	*P. alcalifaciens* *P. rettgeri* *P. stuartii*	wide variety of healthcare acquired infections of respiratory tract, urinary tract, blood, and several other normally sterile sites; most frequently in seriously debilitated patients	endogenous; person to person
Pseudomonas	enteric, aerobic Gram-negative rod; worldwide distribution in water, soil, plants, found in aqueous solutions, sink traps, hydrotherapy and respiratory equipment	*P. aeruginosa*	community-acquired infections in nonimmunocompromised: folliculitis acquired in swimming pools, water slides, whirlpools, hot tubs; swimmer's ear, more severe ear infections in diabetics and elderly with temporal bone and basilar skull osteomyelitis; meningitis; eye infections associated with contact lens use; osteomyelitis of calcaneus in children from nail penetrating a sneaker; endocarditis in intravenous-drug users; leading cause of healthcare acquired respiratory tract infections; UTI, wound infections, peritonitis in persons on chronic ambulatory peritoneal dialysis and bacteremia particularly in burn patients; an unusual "mucoid" phenotype chronically infects 70-80% of adolescents and adults with cystic fibrosis	contaminated water, solutions; foods; exposure to contaminated equipment
	found in soil and water	*P. alcaligenes*	catheter-related endocarditis in bone marrow transplant recipient	environmental contact
	found in soil and water	*P. fluorescens*	occasional transfusion-associated septicemia	blood transfusions
	found in soil and water; fruits and vegetables; moist hospital environments	*P. oryzihabitans*	bacteremia in immunocompromised persons with central venous catheters; peritonitis in persons undergoing chronic ambulatory peritoneal dialysis; cellulitis, abscesses, wound infections; meningitis following neurosurgical procedures; HAI catheter infections; septicemia	environmental contact

	found in soil and water	*P. putida*	catheter-related bacteremia in persons with cancer	environmental contact
	found in soil and water	*P. stutzeri*	bacteremia in immunosuppressed and in persons undergoing hemodialysis with contaminated dialysis fluid; wounds, UTI, and osteomyelitis; pneumonia in alcoholics and in intubated patients; meningitis in HIV positive patients	environmental contact; contaminated water and solutions
Rhizobium	Gram-negative rod; found in soil and plants	*R. radiobacter*	associated with plastic materials (biomedical prosthetics, intravenous and peritoneal catheters), and rarely septicemia	contact
Rhodococcus	aerobic Gram-positive coccoid to rod shaped; normally found in soil and water, associated with livestock	*R. equi*	opportunistic infections in immunocompromised; pulmonary, bacteremia, skin, endophthalmitis, peritonitis, catheter-associated sepsis, prostatic abscesses	inhalation
Rickettsia	obligate intracellular Gram-negative coccobacilli; intracellular parasites		Rocky Mountain Spotted Fever (RMSF); Murine Typhus; Louse-borne fever; ; Flea-borne spotted fever; Boutonneuse fever; systemic diseases (spotted fever, typhus, scrub typhus) with rash, headache, and fever; infections may be severe, sometimes fatal; organisms infect wild animals and their arthropod parasites; humans are victims of incidental infections	arthropod borne
	etiologic agent of rickettsialpox; occurs worldwide; natural reservoir: mice and rats	*R. akari*	Rickettsialpox: mild disease characterized by a chickenpox-like rash and fever; initial site of bite develops a black eschar	mite bites
	occurs worldwide; found in man and flying squirrels	*R. prowazekii*	epidemic typhus (classic typhus): fever, prostration and rash starting on the trunk region; **Category B bioterrorism agent**	body louse

(continued)

Genus	Description	Name + (FKA)	Infections	Mode(s) of Transmission
	reservoir: deer, dogs, rodents, foxes, rabbits, birds, and man	R. rickettsii	Rocky Mountain spotted fever: fever, headache, muscle pain progressing to a rash, which starts peripherally, in contrast to that of epidemic and endemic typhus	bite of ixodid (hard) ticks
	found in Eurasia and Asia; reservoir: rodents	R. sibirica	North Asia tick typhus or Siberian tick typhus, a mild form of spotted fever	tick bites
	reservoir: rats, other rodents, and opossums	R. typhi	endemic (murine) typhus similar but milder than epidemic typhus	rat fleas/feces
Salmonella	enteric, facultative anaerobic Gram-negative rod; normally found in water; S. typhi found only in humans; non-typhi (zoonotic) forms found in pet turtles, chickens, uncooked eggs	S. serotype Choleraesuis S. serotype Enteritidis S. serotype Typhi S. serotype Typhimurium	salmonellosis; typhoid fever: mild enteritis, "food poisoning" or gastroenteritis and rapidly fatal septicemia; **Category B bioterrorism agent**	fecal-oral, sources include: contaminated milk, water, reptiles, amphibians, eggs, ice cream, meringue, shellfish, undercooked chicken, fish, and pork
Serratia	enteric, facultative Gram-negative rod; normal GI tract flora	S. marcescens S. liquefaciens	pneumonia, bacteremia associated with contaminated multidose vials, UTI, surgical site infections; HAI pathogens and colonizers; contact lens-induced red eye	contact; contaminated fluids (intravenous); medical equipment (respiratory therapy)
Shigella	enteric, facultative anaerobic Gram-negative rod; found in the environment	S. dysenteriae (group A)	shigellosis; bloody diarrhea (dysentery) and nonbloody diarrhea, fever, abdominal cramps; complications include hemolytic uremic syndrome (HUS) and Reiter's disease; **Category B bioterrorism agent**	fecal-oral; ingestion of contaminated food and water; food handlers; sexual transmission among homosexual men; contact
		S. flexneri (group B)	bloody diarrhea	same as group A transmission
		S. boydii (group C)	bloody diarrhea	same as group A transmission
		S. sonnei (group D)	bloody diarrhea	same as group A transmission
Sphingomonas	Strict aerobe, negative rod; widely distributed in the environment and water	S. paucimobilis (Pseudomonas paucimobilis)	bacteremia; UTI; peritoneal fluid, wounds and respiratory infections; significance in clinical specimens questioned	water and environmental contact; endogenous

Staphylococcus	Gram-positive cocci in grape-like clusters; normal flora of skin, anterior nares, nasopharynx, and perineal area; *S. aureus* is considered the most important human pathogen	*S. aureus*	abscess, pneumonia, empyema, osteomyelitis, purpural sepsis, bacteremia, endocarditis; strains with acquired resistance to Methicillin (MRSA) common in hospitals; enterotoxins: toxic shock syndrome (TSS), food "poisoning", *Staphylococcus* scalded skin syndrome (SSSS); enterotoxin B = **Category B bioterrorism agent**	endogenous; contact; unwashed hands and contaminated patient care equipment
	normal flora of skin and mucous membranes	*S. epidermidis* aka Coagulase-negative *Staphylococcus*	prosthetic devices, indwelling catheters, sepsis, meningitis, endocarditis, UTI	endogenous; contact; unwashed hands and contaminated patient care equipment
	normal flora of skin and mucous membranes	*S. haemolyticus* aka Coagulase-negative *Staphylococcus*	native valve endocarditis, septicemia, peritonitis, UTI, wound, bone and joint	contact; unwashed hands and contaminated patient care equipment
	normal flora of skin and mucous membranes	*S. lugdunensis* aka Coagulase-negative *Staphylococcus*	foreign body related infections; native-valve endocarditis; chronic osteomyelitis; abscesses	contact; endogenous; contaminated medical equipment
	normal flora of skin and GU tract mucosa	*S. saprophyticus* aka Coagulase-negative *Staphylococcus*	opportunistic UTI in females and nongonococcal urethritis in males, wounds, septicemia	contact; unwashed hands and contaminated patient care equipment
Stenotrophomonas	aerobic Gram-negative rod; naturally inhabits water, soil, plants, vegetables; colonizer in immunosuppressed and cystic fibrosis patients	*S. maltophilia*	bacteremia, meningitis, UTI, pneumonia, mastoiditis, epididymitis, conjunctivitis, endocarditis, peritonitis, bursitis, keratitis, endophthalmitis, cholangitis, mucocutaneous and soft tissue infections, ocular infections, wounds	environment; contact; droplets
Stomatococcus	Gram-positive cocci; normal oral and upper respiratory tract flora	*S. mucilaginosus*	endocarditis, bacteremia, intravascular catheter infection, meningitis, peritonitis; predisposing risk factors are neutropenia, chemotherapy, radiotherapy, and intravenous drug use	endogenous

(continued)

Genus	Description	Name + (FKA)	Infections	Mode(s) of Transmission
Streptobacillus	facultative anaerobic Gram-negative bacillus; natural habitat in rats and mice	*S. moniliformis*	systemic infection, Haverhill fever ("rat-bite fever"): fever, chills, headache, vomiting, severe migratory arthralgias, large joint swelling, nonpruritic rash on palms, soles, and extremities	bite or contact with contaminated blood from infected animals
Streptococcus	Gram-positive cocci in chains or pairs; inhabits skin and upper respiratory tract; colonizes nasopharynx	*S. pyogenes* aka group A beta-hemolytic *Streptococcus*	pharyngitis ("strep throat"), respiratory, ear infections, Ludwig's angina, skin (impetigo, erysipelas, necrotizing fasciitis), soft tissue infections, abscesses, endocarditis, meningitis, sepsis, septic arthritis, rheumatic fever, scarlet fever, glomerulonephritis, toxic shock-like syndrome	endogenous; contact; droplets, respiratory secretions
	normal flora GI tract and female GU tract	*S. agalactiae* aka group B beta-hemolytic *Streptococcus*	neonatal sepsis, meningitis, pneumonia; postpartum infections; urinary and genital tract infections, bacteremia, endocarditis, skin and soft tissue infections, abscesses, osteomyelitis	endogenous; contact; genital tract secretions
	normal flora skin, nasopharynx, GI and GU tracts	*S. dysgalactiae* subsp. *equisimilis* aka group C beta-hemolytic *Streptococcus*	bacteremia, endocarditis, meningitis, septic arthritis, skin infections, abscesses, respiratory tract infections	endogenous; contact
	colonizes nasopharynx	*S. pneumoniae* aka pneumococcus (*Diplococcus pneumonia*)	pneumonia, sepsis, sinusitis, otitis media, endocarditis, meningitis	secretions; endogenous; vaccine available
	viridans group; normal oropharyngeal, GI and female genital tract flora	*S. anginosus* *S. gordonii* *S. intermedius* *S. mitis* *S. oralis* *S. sanguinis*	subacute bacterial endocarditis, especially in persons with prosthetic heart valves, deep-seated brain, liver, and oral abscesses, female genital infections; sometimes considered a contaminant	oropharyngeal secretions; endogenous

Streptomyces	Gram-positive rod with branching filaments; found in sandy soil	*S. paraguayensis* *S. somaliensis* *S. sudanensis*	mycetoma; chronic soft tissue infections	environmental contact; inhalation
Treponema	Gram-negative spirochete; reservoir: humans	*T. pallidum* subsp. *pallidum*	syphilis: acute and chronic sexually transmitted disease characterized by primary lesion; secondary eruption involving skin and mucous membranes; long periods of latency and late lesions of skin, bone, viscera, CNS, and cardiovascular system; fatal infections can occur in late tertiary stage	sexual contact; direct contact with exudate from lesions; blood transfusion if donor in early stages of infection; fetal infection through placental transfer at delivery
Ureaplasma	smallest free living microorganism contained only by a cell membrane; present in genitourinary tract	*U. urealyticum* (T strains of *Mycoplasma*)	bacterial vaginosis, nonchlamydial-nongonococcal urethritis (NGU), PID; chorioamnionitis; extragenital disease in immunocompromised persons and premature newborn infants; present in mixed infections	endogenous; direct intimate contact
Veillonella	anaerobic Gram-negative diplococci; normal flora of upper respiratory and GI tracts, and vagina	*V. atypica* *V. dispar* *V. parvula*	bacteremia; meningitis; osteomyelitis; prosthetic joint infections; endocarditis; discitis; vertebral osteomyelitis; rare opportunistic organism; oral, bite wounds, head, neck, and miscellaneous soft tissue infections	endogenous
Vibrio	Facultative anaerobic Gram-negative rod; natural inhabitants of fresh, brackish, and salt water worldwide; more than 30 species and 12 are human pathogens	*V. cholerae* O1, subtypes: Inaba, Ogawa, Hikojima, biotypes: Classical, *El Tor* (*V. comma*)	cholera pandemics, epidemics, and outbreaks occur worldwide; cholera toxin: acute bacterial enteric disease severe form with sudden onset, profuse, painless watery stools, occasional vomiting, and, if untreated, rapid dehydration, acidosis, circulatory collapse, and renal failure; asymptomatic and mild cases are common; Category B bioterrorism agent	fecal-oral; ingestion of raw or inadequately cooked seafood from contaminated waters (coastal and estuarine)
	aquatic birds are carriers; occurs inland as well as along Gulf Coast and Great Lakes region	*V. cholerae* non-O1, (non-agglutinable *V.cholerae*)	gastroenteritis; systemic infections generally occur in immunocompromised	fecal-oral; contaminated seafood

(continued)

Genus	Description	Name + (FKA)	Infections	Mode(s) of Transmission
	isolated in 1993 from outbreak around Bay of Bengal	*V. cholerae* O139 (Bengal Cholera)	produces toxin and cholera illness	fecal-oral; contaminated seafood
	outbreak in Bangladesh, rare in U.S. Gulf Coast regions	*V. fluvialis*	gastroenteritis and rare sepsis	contact with coastal water and possibly contaminated seafood
		V. mimicus	rare cause of diarrhea that can produce cholera-like symptoms; and otitis media	consumption of seafood, typically, raw oysters
	number of outbreaks in Japan; reservoir: fish	*V. parahaemolyticus* (Kanagawa phenomenon)	enteric infection characterized by watery diarrhea and abdominal cramps, nausea, vomiting, fever, headache, bloody mucoid stools, high WBC count	contaminated raw fish; sea water
		V. vulnificus (lactose positive *Vibrio*)	septicemia in persons with chronic liver disease, chronic alcoholism, hemochromatosis or immunocompromised; bullous skin lesions, thrombocytopenia, wounds sustained in coastal or estuarine waters range from mild self-limited lesions to cellulitis and myositis; necrotizing fasciitis; endotoxic shock	ingestion of raw or inadequately cooked seafood or exposure to coastal/estuarine seawater
VRE (Vanco-mycin Resistant *Enterococcus*)	See *Enterococcus*			
Xanthomonas	See *Stenotrophomonas maltophilia*			
Yersinia	zoonotic, facultative anaerobic, enteric Gram-negative rod, 11 species and 3 are known human pathogens; usually infect rats and rodents (ground squirrels, prairie dogs); humans are accidental hosts	*Y. pestis (Pasturella pestis)*	Bubonic plague: fever, chills, malaise, myalgia, nausea, sore throat, and headache; lymphadenitis results in swelling, inflammation, tenderness, and lesions (buboes); progresses to blood stream dissemination, septicemia, and pneumonia; **Category A bioterrorism agent**	bites from infected rat fleas; handling of tissues of infected animals

Organism	Characteristics	Disease	Transmission
		Septicemic plague: direct inoculation of the bloodstream without localization in regional lymph nodes	bites from infected rat fleas; handling of tissues of infected animals
		Pneumonic plague: secondary infection of the lungs resulting in pneumonia, mediastinitis or pleural effusion; localized outbreaks or devastating epidemics; **Category A bioterrorism agent**	droplet; also present in animals including domestic pets (cats)
Y. enterocolitica	infections more common in northern latitudes; found in pigs, rabbits, livestock, rodents, dogs, and cats	intestinal and extraintestinal yersiniosis: hemorrhagic enterocolitis, terminal ileitis, mesenteric lymphadenitis (pseudo-appendicular syndrome), septicemia, and focal infections; post-infectious arthritis in adolescents and young adults; associated with contaminated blood transfusion products	fecal-oral; ingestion of contaminated food (often milk and pork) and water; contact with infected animals
Y. pseudotuberculosis	found in rodents, rabbits, deer, and birds	self-limiting infection similar to *Y. enterocolitica*, abdominal pain is more common and active diarrhea is less common; mesenteric lymphadenitis; erythema nodosum; Reiter's syndrome; nephritis	fecal-oral; ingestion of contaminated food or water; contact with infected animals

References

Brooks GF, Butel JS, Morse SA. *Jawetz, Melnick, & Adelberg's Medical Microbiology*. 24th ed. New York: Appleton-Lange Medical Books/McGraw-Hill; 2010.

Forbes B, Sahm DF, Weissfeld AS. *Bailey & Scott's Diagnostic Microbiology*. 12th ed. St. Louis: Mosby-Yearbook/Harcourt Health Sciences; 2007.

Gilbert DN, Moellering RC, Eliopoulos GM, Chambers HF, Saag MS. *The Sanford Guide to Antimicrobial Therapy 2011*. 41st ed. Sperryville, VA: Antimicrobial Therapy, Inc.; 2011.

Grota P, ed. *APIC Text of Infection Control and Epidemiology*, 4th ed. Washington, DC: Association for Professionals in Infection Control and Epidemiology, 2014.

Heymann DL, ed. *Control of Communicable Diseases Manual*, 19th ed. Baltimore: American Public Health Association, United Book Press, Inc.; 2008.

Mahon CR, Lehman, DC, Manuselis G, eds. *Textbook of Diagnostic Microbiology*, 4th ed. St. Louis: W.B. Saunders Company/Harcourt Health Sciences; 2010.

Mandell GL, Bennett JE, Dolin R, eds. *Principles and Practice of Infectious Diseases*, 7th ed. St. Louis: Churchill Livingstone/Harcourt Health Sciences; 2010.

Pickering LK, ed. *2009 Red Book, Report of the Committee on Infectious Diseases*, 28th ed. Elk Grove: American Academy of Pediatrics; 2009.

Porter, RS and Kaplan, JL, eds. *The Merck Manual of Diagnosis and Therapy*, 19th ed. Whitehouse Station: Merck & Company; 2011.

Tortora GJ, Funke BR, Case CL. *Microbiology, An Introduction*, 10th ed. San Francisco: Benjamin Cummings Publishing; 2009.

Versalovic J, Carroll KC, Jorgensen JH, Funke G, Landry ML, Warnock DW, eds. *Manual of Clinical Microbiology*, 12th ed. Washington, DC: American Society of Microbiology Press; 2011.

Additional Resources

APIC Text Online. 2011. http://text.apic.org/

American Society for Microbiology. http://www.asm.org

Centers for Disease Control and Prevention. http://www.cdc.gov

Emerging & Re-emerging Infectious Diseases. In: NIH Education, Understanding Infectious Diseases. Available at http://science.education.nih.gov/supplements/nih1/diseases/guide/understanding1.htm Accessed 1/4/2012.

Health-care Associated Infections. http://www.cdc.gov/hai/

Micromedex Healthcare Series. www.micromedex.com/products/hcs/

SHEA Guidelines and Resources. Compendium of Strategies to Prevent HAIs. Available at http://www.shea-online.org/GuidelinesResources/CompendiumofStrategiestoPreventHAIs.aspx

The Sanford Guide to Antimicrobial Therapy 41st edition, 2011. http://www.sanfordguide.com

World Health Organization. http://www.who.int

Chapter Two

Fungi

Fungi (yeasts and molds) are widely distributed in nature. Of the more than 100,000 species of fungi, fewer than 500 species cause disease or infections in humans and other animals. Less than 50 species cause infections in healthy persons. However, fungi are common causes of infection in patients with altered immune systems. Mycology is the study of fungi. Mycosis refers to infections or diseases caused by fungi.

Growth

Typically fungi are separated into two broad groups, yeasts and molds, based on the appearance of the colonies formed. Yeasts are unicellular, round to oval organisms ranging in size from 2 to 60 μm. Yeasts reproduce by budding and production of spores and produce moist, creamy, opaque or pasty colonies. Basic structures of molds are tube-like projections known as hyphae. Molds reproduce by elongation and fragmentation of their hyphae and produce fluffy, cottony, wooly, or powdery colonies. Several pathogenic species of fungi that grow either as yeast or mold are referred to as dimorphic, meaning two forms of growth.

Taxonomy

The term fungus refers generically to all members of the Kingdom Fungi and includes yeast, molds (mildews, rusts and smuts) and fleshy fungi (mushrooms and puffballs). All fungi share the following characteristics:

- Presence of chitin in the cell wall
- Presence of ergosterol in the cell membrane
- Reproduction by spore formation
- Lack of chlorophyll
- Lack of susceptibility to antibacterial antibiotics
- Heterotropic nature (derive nutrition from organic materials)

The four major categories of mycosis are:

1. Superficial or cutaneous mycoses: Infections or diseases that involve hair, skin or nails without direct invasion of deeper tissues. This cat-

egory includes dermatophytes which is a common term used to designate a group of three species of fungi that commonly cause skin disease in people or animals. These three species are *Epidermophyton, Trichophyton* and *Microsporum.*

2. Subcutaneous mycoses: Infections or diseases, chromoblastomycosis and mycetoma that involve the skin or subcutaneous tissues.

3. Systemic mycoses: Infections or diseases primarily involving the lungs, but may also become widely disseminated and involve any organ system. This category includes *Blastomyces, Coccidioides, Histoplasma, Paracoccidioides* and *Penicillium marneffei.*

4. Opportunistic mycoses: Opportunistic infections are systemic and occur primarily in patients with altered immune status either by underlying disease or use of immunosuppressive agents. This category includes *Aspergillus, Candida* and *Cryptococcus.*

Mycotoxins

Mycotoxins are metabolites of many ubiquitous fungi species. Mycotoxins can have adverse effects on humans and animals and are of concern in food safety. Mycotoxins cause veterinary problems and illnesses; may be of relevance in Sick Building Syndrome; noted in flooding in New Orleans, Louisiana post Hurricane Katrina; and could potentially be used as a bioterrorism agent.

Common mycotoxins, fungi which produce them, and the food sources in which mycotoxins are found

Mycotoxin	Fungi	Source
Aflatoxins	*Aspergillus*	Cereal, rice, figs, nuts
Citrinin	*Penicillium, Aspergillus*	Japanese yellow rice, grains, peanuts, fruits
Ergot Alkaloids	*Aspergillus*	Grains
Fumonisins	*Fusarium*	Corn
Patulin	*Penicillium*	Unfermented juices
Ochratoxins	*Penicillium, Aspergillus*	Barley, oats, rye, wheat, coffee beans
Trichothecens	*Stachybotrys, Fusarium*	Barley, oats, rye, wheat, straw
Zearalenone	*Fusarium*	Corn, grains

Contamination of food by mycotoxins can occur anywhere along the food chain from storage to shipping. Monitoring of mycotoxins is necessary due to the potential to affect the health of human, livestock, and plant populations and the subsequent effect on international economy.

Table

The following table will help guide the user through an understanding of fungi. Note that the table:

- Lists the fungi by Genus
- Provides a description of the fungi as well as reservoirs or where normally found
- Lists the names and formerly known as names, (**"Name + FKA"**) if applicable
- Describes infections and the mode of transmission

Genus	Description	Name + (FKA)	Infections	Mode(s) of Transmission
Acremonium	mold; found in soil, decaying plants; worldwide, common in Asia, North, South, and Central America, Oceania, Europe	*A. kiliense* *A. recifei (Cephalosporium species)*	mycetoma; onychomycosis; corneal ulcers, meningitis, endocarditis, endophthalmitis, osteomyelitis, peritonitis; opportunistic infections in immunocompromised	traumatic inoculation
Alternaria	mold; found in tomatoes, plants, food stuffs, soil, indoor air; common in tropics and subtropics	*A. alternata* *A. infectoria*	sinusitis, keratitis, onychomycosis, keratomycosis, subcutaneous, cutaneous and invasive infections, otitis media, osteomyelitis; opportunistic in bone marrow transplant	contact; inhalation
Apophysomyces	mold; found in tropic and subtropical soil	*A. elegans*	skin, soft tissue, necrotizing fasciitis, osteomyelitis, bladder and renal infections; mucormycosis; systemic zygomycosis (rare cause of infections)	traumatic injury to skin, insect bites, surgical and burn wounds; inhalation
Arthrographis	mold; found in soil and compost; worldwide	*A. kalrae*	onychomycosis; opportunistic infections	contact; trauma; inhalation
Aspergillus	mold; found in soil, natural debris, air handling systems, indoor and outdoor air; worldwide	*A. flavus* *A. fumigatus* *A. lentulus* *A. nidulans* *A. niger* *A. terreus*	invasive pulmonary aspergillosis; otomycosis; opportunistic infections; aspergilloma, toxicosis, allergic reactions, sarcoidosis; secondary colonizers after *Candida*	contact; trauma; inhalation; ingestion
Aureobasidium	yeast-like mold; found in plant debris, soil, wood, textiles, and indoor air environment; worldwide	*A. pullulans*	rare infections; phaehyphomycosis; keratomycosis, pulmonary mycosis with sepsis; cutaneous mycoses; other opportunistic infections; catheter-related septicemia; peritonitis; "humidifier lung"	contact
Basidiobolus	mold; found in decaying vegetables and plants, debris, dung, soil; worldwide, more abundant in Indonesia, Uganda, Nigeria, tropical regions	*B. ranarum*	subcutaneous chronic infections, mostly in male children; basidiobolomycosis; rare GI infections	inhalation; trauma

Beauveria	mold; found in decaying vegetable matter, soil; worldwide	B. bassiana	rare mycotic keratitis; pneumonia in immuno-compromised	contact; inhalation
Bipolaris	mold; found in soil, plants; world-wide	B. australiensis B. hawaiiensis B. spicifera	meningitis, sinusitis, peritonitis, keratitis, cutaneous and pulmonary infections, fungemia; otitis media in farm workers	contact; inhalation
Blastomyces	mold to yeast phases under appropriate conditions of temperature and nutrition; found in soil; common in states surrounding the Ohio, Mississippi Rivers, Great Lakes Region, South East and South Central U.S.; associated with beaver dams	B. dermatitidis	blastomycosis; self-limited or asymptomatic localized pulmonary lesions; cutaneous and disseminated and systemic mycoses in immunocompromised; chronic infections of skin, genitourinary tract, bone, kidneys	inhalation; contact
Blastoschizomyces	yeast and mold phases; normal skin flora, ubiquitous worldwide in nature, soil, sand, poultry feces	B. capitatus (Trichosporon capitatum; Geotrichum capitatum)	invasive disease in leukemic patients; fungemia, disseminated infections in lung, kidney, spleen, brain, endocardium, bone, meningitis, encephalitis, urinary tract infection; mycetoma; onychomycosis	contact; inhalation; endogenous
Candida	yeast; normal gastrointestinal, oral, skin flora; worldwide	C. africana [common] C. albicans [common] C. catenulata [medically important= MI] C. ciferrii [MI] C. dubliniensis [common] C. glabrata [common] C. guilliermondii [MI] C. haemulonii [MI] C. krusei [emerging] C. lipolytica [emerging] C. lusitaniae [emerging] C. parapsilosis [common] C. rugosa [MI] C. tropicalis [common] C. utilis [MI]	opportunistic; candidiasis; IV and central line infections (superficial to systemic); thrush, vaginitis, skin and nail infections, pulmonary disease, enteritis, esophagitis, endocarditis, meningitis, brain abscess, pyelonephritis, cystitis; chronic endocarditis in IV drug users; surgical site infections; fungemia	contact; endogenous

(continued)

Genus	Description	Name + (FKA)	Infections	Mode(s) of Transmission
Chaetomium	mold; found in soil, air, plant debris; all types of climates from extremes of Himalayas to deserts	*C. atrobrunneum* *C. globosum* *C. perlucidium*	contaminant; cutaneous infections, brain abscesses, peritonitis; onychomycosis	contact
Chrysosporium	mold; found in soil, plant material, dung, and birds; lives on remains of hairs and feathers in soil; worldwide, common in North America, Europe, Iran	*C. zonatum*	skin infections; onychomycosis; systemic infections in bone marrow transplant recipients and in patients with chronic granulomatous disease	contact; inhalation
Cladophialophora	mold; found in soil, air, plant debris; worldwide; majority of cases in subtropical regions of Americas and Africa	*C. bantiana* *C. carrionii*	chromoblastomycosis; mycetoma; brain abscesses; skin lesions	contact
Cladosporium	mold; found in soil, plants, organic material, surface of fiberglass duct liners, paints, textiles; worldwide	*C. cladosporioides* *C. oxysporum*	common contaminant; skin, nail and pulmonary infections; keratitis	contact; trauma; inhalation
Coccidioides	mold (environment and culture) and yeast (mature states) phases; found in soil; endemic in Southwest U.S., extending into Mexico, Central and South America	*C. immitis* *C. posadasii*	coccidioidomycosis; transient and chronic pulmonary infections; systemic mycosis (immunosuppressed at increased risk) begins in respiratory tract and disseminates to meninges, bone, skin, joints, lymph nodes and subcutaneous tissue	inhalation
Conidiobolus	mold; found in soil in tropical and subtropical Africa and Southeast Asia	*C. coronatus* *C. incongruus*	chronic granulomatous diseases, commonly involving nose and face in adult males and outdoor workers	inhalation; trauma
Cryptococcus	yeast; found in soil, decaying vegetables, dung, bird feces, eucalyptus trees; worldwide, common in tropics, southern hemisphere, Pacific Northwest U.S.	*C. gattii* *C. luteolus* *C. neoformans* *C. terreus* *C. uniguttulatus*	crytococcosis; opportunistic; acute and chronic pulmonary infections, disseminated CNS, cutaneous, eye, sinus, ear and other organ infections	contact; inhalation

Cunninghamella	mold; found in Mediterranean and subtropic soil	*C. bertholletiae*	rare infections; mucormycosis; disseminated zygomycosis; rhino-cerebral, pulmonary and cutaneous infections; opportunistic in immunocompromised	inhalation; trauma
Curvularia	mold; found in soil, decaying vegetation, plant material; worldwide	*C. geniculata* *C. lunata*	common contaminant; wound infections; mycetoma, onychomycosis; keratitis, sinusitis, cerebral abscesses, pneumonia, dialysis-associated infections; opportunistic in immunocompromised	inhalation; contact
Epidermophyton	mold; found in moist showers and gyms; worldwide	*E. floccosum*	dermatophytoses; superficial, cutaneous mycosis: ringworm of the foot, body, groin, and nails	contact
Exophiala	mold; found worldwide in decaying wood, soil, plant debris, fruits, vegetables; common skin colonization in irritated, excoriated skin and eczema	*E. dermatitidis (Wangiella dermatitidis)* *E. jeanselmei*	cutaneous, subcutaneous, mucosal, systemic disease; granuloma; mycetoma; chromoblastomycosis, intramuscular abscess with fistula formation; endocarditis, septic arthritis, cerebral infections; may be fatal in immunocompromised	contact; trauma
Exserohilum	mold; found in plant material, particularly grasses, and soil; common in warm, humid climates	*E. rostratum*	rare infections; phaeohyphomycosis; mimicking hemorrhagic herpes zoster; keratitis	contact
Fonsecaea	mold; found in soil, wood; common in Central and South America	*F. monophora* *F. pedrosoi*	chromoblastomycosis	environmental contact; trauma
Fusarium	mold; found worldwide in soil, plants, grains, humidifiers	*F. chlamydosporum* *F. falciforme (Acremonium falciforme)* *F. moniliforme* *F. oxysporum* *F. solani*	keratitis; subcutaneous diseases; nail infections; systemic, invasive diseases; devastating to burn and bone-marrow transplant patients	inhalation; contact; trauma, ingestion

(continued)

Genus	Description	Name + (FKA)	Infections	Mode(s) of Transmission
Histoplasma	mold (environment) and yeast (culture) phases; found in soil contaminated with bird and bat feces; worldwide, common endemic mycosis in states surrounding the Mississippi and Ohio Rivers, and Africa, Australia, eastern Asia	*H. capsulatum var. capsulatum* *H. capsulatum var. duboisii*	acute pulmonary histoplasmosis often self-limited; chronic and cavitary histoplasmosis in individuals with underlying lung disease; disseminated/systemic mycosis in immuno-compromised and elderly; may be fatal; *H. capsulatum*=N. American histoplasmosis (pulmonary and disseminated); *H. duboisii*=African histoplasmosis (skin and bone)	inhalation; contact
Hortaea	mold; found in soil, particularly in tropical and subtropical climates	*H. werneckii (Exophiala werneckii)*	Tinea nigra, superficial infection of stratum corneum (usually palms and soles of feet)	direct inoculation onto skin; contact
Lacazia	yeast-like mold; found in tropical zone waters, restricted to South America	*L. loboi (Loboa loboi)*	lobomycosis is a tropical mycosis characterized by mucocutaneous lesions, usually nodular, vegetating, verrucose, cauliflower-like and hyper- or hypopigmented	cutaneous trauma, insect bite or skin wound via contact with infected surrounding, such as dolphins
Leptosphaeria	mold; found in soil, organic debris; West Africa, India	*L. senegalensis* *L. tompkinisii*	mycetoma; black piedra	contact; trauma
Lichtheimia	mold; found in soil, compost, decaying vegetation, rotten fruits and breads, indoor air; worldwide	*L. corymbifera (Absidia corymbifera)*	opportunistic in immunocompromised; pulmonary, rhino-cerebral, cutaneous, GI, renal and meningeal infections which may disseminate; mucormycosis; zygomycosis	direct inoculation (wounds); inhalation; intravenous drug use
Madurella	mold; found in soil, decaying vegetation; common in the tropics, India, Africa, South America, Middle East	*M. grisea* *M. mycetomatis*	subcutaneous infection from traumatic foreign bodies, rare destruction of bone; human pathogen (rarely seen in US); madura foot; mycetoma	contact; trauma
Malassezia	yeast; found in soil, animals; worldwide	*M. furfur (Pityrosporum)* *M. globosa* *M. restricta* *M. slooffiae* *M. sympodialis*	tinia versicolor; superficial mycosis (skin, hair); rare disseminated infection in patients receiving high dose lipid replacements; colonization of IV catheters	contact

Genus	Description	Species	Infections/Diseases	Transmission
Microascus	mold; found worldwide in soil, plant material, feathers, animal dung, insects	*M. cinereus* *M. cirrosus* *M. trigonosporus* *M. manginii*	significant invasive infections in immunocompromised patient; onychomycosis; maxillary sinusitis; suppurative cutaneous granulomata ; endocarditis; brain abscess	contact
Microsporum	mold; found worldwide in soil, humans, animals	*M. audouinii* *M. canis* *M. ferrugineum* *M. gypseum* *M. praecox* *M. racemosum*	dermatophytosis; superficial, cutaneous mycosis: ringworm of the foot, scalp, nail, body, groin, beard, hand: (tinea pedis, capitis, unguium, corporis)	direct and indirect skin contact with skin and fomites (barber clippers, clothing, contaminated showers)
Mucor	mold; found worldwide in soil, plants, food products	*M. circinelloides* *M. indicus* *M. racemosus* *M. ramosissimus*	mucormycosis; zygomycosis with tissue necrosis, vascular invasion, thrombosis; severe opportunistic infections in immunocompromised; mucocutaneous, rhino-cerebral, septic arthritis, dialysis-associated infections	inhalation or ingestion of spores; contact
Neotestudina	yeast; found in soil in tropical areas, central Africa	*Neotestudina rosatii*	white grain mycetoma; chronic subcutaneous infection leads to abscesses with possible osteomyelitis	traumatic implantation into the subcutaneous tissue via contact with soil
Paecilomyces	mold; found worldwide in soil, plants, animals	*P. lilacinus* *P. variotii*	keratomycosis; endocarditis, sinusitis, cellulitis, subcutaneous, cutaneous and disseminated pulmonary infections; toxicosis	contact; trauma; inhalation
Paracoccidioides	mold (room temperature) and yeast (under appropriate nutritional and temperature conditions) phases; found in soil, dust, wood; South and Central America	*P. brasiliensis*	paracoccidioimycosis; oral ulcerative, cutaneous and subcutaneous lesions; lymphadenopathy; pulmonary and systemic mycoses; emerging endemic public health problem among HIV population in Southeast Asia	inhalation; contact; trauma; ingestion of contaminated soil or dust
Penicillium	mold (room temperature) and yeast (body temperature) phases; found in soil, plant material, indoor air; Southeast Asia and China; over 30 species	*P. marneffei*	keratitis; endocarditis; pulmonary and skin infections; external otomycosis; peritonitis; systemic disease; opportunistic infection of HIV positive individuals in Southeast Asia	contact; soil exposure; trauma; inhalation
Phialophora	mold; found in water, soil, decaying vegetation; tropical and subtropical regions	*P. americana* *P. europaea* *P. verrucosa*	chromoblastomycosis, mycosis of the skin and subcutaneous tissues usually lower extremities; keratitis; granulomas	contact; trauma

(continued)

Genus	Description	Name + (FKA)	Infections	Mode(s) of Transmission
Pichia	yeast; found in decaying plants; skin colonizer; common in temperate and tropical regions	*P. anomala* *P. angusta*	generally considered a contaminant; rare and emerging opportunistic mycoses in immuno-compromised patient (i.e. prematurity, low birth weight, long duration of hospital stay); UTIs; peritonitis; prosthetic valve endocarditis; fungemia	contact
Piedraia	mold; found in soil and fomites; common in tropical climates of Central and South America, Southeast Asia, South Pacific Islands	*P. hortae*	black piedra: infections of the hair and scalp common in the tropics, rarely involves axillary or pubic hair	direct skin to skin contact; indirect contact with contaminated barber clippers, hats, combs
Pneumocystis	yeast; formerly classified as a tissue protozoon (single-cell); worldwide	*P. carinii* *P. jiroveci*	asymptomatic to mildly symptomatic; pneumonitis and interstitial pneumonia in immunocompromised; multiple extrapulmonary sites associated with rapidly fatal outcome	transmission suggestions: 1. airborne; 2. acquired early in life; 3. person-to-person transmission; 4. short periods of exposure with small inoculums
Pseudallescheria	mold; found in soil, decaying vegetation; worldwide, most common in North and South America	*P. boydii (Petrilidium boydii)* Asexual form = *Scedosporium apiospermum*	mycetoma, suppuration of subcutaneous tissue with sinus tracts (feet, lower leg, hand, shoulders, back, nasal sinuses), meningitis, arthritis, endocarditis, keratitis, external otomycosis, brain abscesses, pulmonary infections	contact; trauma
Pyrenochaeta	mold; found in soil, decaying vegetation; arid subtropics, Central and South America	*P. mackinnonii* *P. romeroi*	mycetoma; suppuration of subcutaneous tissue with formation of sinus tracts (foot, lower leg, hand, shoulder and back)	contact; trauma
Pythium	mold; found in soil and plants; worldwide, more common in tropical and subtropical regions	*P. insidiosum*	rare infections; keratitis, cutaneous and subcutaneous infections	trauma; contact; ingestion

Genus	Description	Species	Infections/Diseases	Transmission
Rhinosporidium	mold (soil and water) and yeast (living tissue) phases; endemic in India, Ceylon; may occur in the Americas, Europe, Africa, more common in tropical regions	R. seeberi	nasal, conjunctiva, urethral infections; chronic granulomatous disease; rhinosporidiosis	contact; inhalation
Rhizomucor	mold; found in soil, composting or fermenting organic matter; common throughout temperate regions of the world	R. miehei, R. pusillus (Mucor pusillus), R. variabilis	mucormycosis; zygomycosis in immune-compromised individuals	inhalation
Rhizopus	mold; found in soil, air, compost, wood products; worldwide	R. microsporus, R. oryzae, R. schipperae, R. azygosporus	mucormycosis; zygomycosis; rhino-facial-cranial infections seen in diabetic, malnourished, burns and immunocompromised	inhalation
Rhodotorula	yeast; found in soil, water, food, plants, moist skin, shower curtains, air, related to dialysis, IV catheters, solutions, and respiratory equipment; worldwide	R. glutinis, R. mucilaginosa (R. rubra)	R. glutinis and R. mucilaginosa are the most common pathogens: meningitis; fungemia; endocarditis; chronic skin diseases; dialysis-related peritonitis	contact; inhalation
Saccharomyces	yeast; brewer's yeast; found in beer, wine yeast, plants, animals, environment; common in wine-producing regions of the world	S. cerevisiae	thrush, UTI, empyema, fungemia	person-to-person; contact; contaminated health foods
Saksenaea	mold; found worldwide in forest soil	S. vasiformis	rare infections; invasive lesions	traumatic implantation into the subcutaneous tissue via contact with soil
Scedosporium	mold; found worldwide in soil and plants	S. apiospermum Sexual form = Pseudoallescheria boydii	subcutaneous infections; keratitis; septic arthritis; osteomylitis	trauma; inhalation
Scopulariopsis	mold; found worldwide in soil, old carpet, wallpaper	S. brevicaulis	contaminant; nail infections (usually toenails); skin, soft tissue, bone and pulmonary infections in immunocompromised; mycetoma can disseminate; occupational allergy in tobacco industry	contact

(continued)

Genus	Description	Name + (FKA)	Infections	Mode(s) of Transmission
Sporobolomyces	yeast; found in air, tree leaves, and orange peels; natural habitats are humans, mammals, birds, the environment, and plants	*S. holsaticus* *S. roseus* *S. salmonicolor*	lymphadenitis in patients with AIDS; dermatitis; cerebral infection; fungemia	contact; inhalation
Sporothrix	mold and yeast phases; found in soil, wood, plants; worldwide; widespread in temperate and tropical zones	*S. brasiliensis* *S. globosa* *S. schenckii* (*Sporotrichum*)	cutaneous, osteoarticular, pulmonary, disseminated and meningeal infections	contact; trauma
Stachybotrys	mold; found in water-damaged cellulose, sheetrock, paper, ceiling tiles, insulation backing and wallpaper; worldwide	*S. chartarum*	pulmonary hemosiderosis; produces extremely toxic mycotoxins; symptoms: dermatitis, cough, rhinitis, nose bleeds, burning sensation in the mouth and nasal passage, headache, general malaise and fever	inhalation of toxins; ingestion; dermal exposure
Trichoderma	mold; found in soil, plant materials; prefers climates with moderate temperatures	*T. citrinoviride* *T. longibrachiatum*	lung infections	inhalation
Trichophyton	mold; found in soil, wet areas in gyms and showers; worldwide in warm regions; native to Mediterranean regions	*T. concentricum* *T. megninii* *T. mentagrophytes* *T. rubrum* *T. schoenleinii* *T. soudanense* *T. tonsurans* *T. verrucosum* *T. violaceum*	dermatophytoses; superficial, cutaneous mycoses; ringworm (skin, hair, nail infections); onychomycosis; tinea pedis (athlete's foot), tinea barbae, tinea capitis, tinea corporis, tinea cruris (jock itch), tinea unguium	contact
Trichosporon	yeast; normal mouth, skin, nails, GI tract flora; found in soil, water, vegetables, mammals, birds; common in South America, Africa, and Asia; sporadic infections in North America and Europe	*T. asahii* *T. asteroides* *T. beigelii* *T. cutaneum* *T. inkin* *T. loubieri* *T. ovoides*	opportunistic pathogen; superficial (white piedra; onychomycosis; otomycosis) and invasive infections in immunocompromised; neutropenia is most important predisposing factor	contact

References

Brooks GF, Butel JS, Morse SA. *Jawetz, Melnick, & Adelberg's Medical Microbiology*, 24th ed. New York: Appleton-Lange Medical Books/McGraw-Hill; 2010.

Forbes B, Sahm DF, Weissfeld AS. *Bailey & Scott's Diagnostic Microbiology*. 12th ed. St. Louis: Mosby-Yearbook/Harcourt Health Sciences; 2007.

Gilbert DN, Moellering RC, Eliopoulos GM, Chambers HF, Saag MS. *The Sanford Guide to Antimicrobial Therapy 2011*. 41st ed. Sperryville, VA: Antimicrobial Therapy, Inc.; 2011.

Grota P, ed. *APIC Text of Infection Control and Epidemiology*, 4th ed. Washington, DC: Association for Professionals in Infection Control and Epidemiology, 2014.

Heymann DL, ed. *Control of Communicable Diseases Manual*, 19th ed. Baltimore: American Public Health Association, United Book Press, Inc.; 2008.

Mahon CR, Lehman, DC, Manuselis G, eds. *Textbook of Diagnostic Microbiology*, 4th ed. St. Louis: W.B. Saunders Company/Harcourt Health Sciences; 2010.

Mandell GL, Bennett JE, Dolin R, eds. *Principles and Practice of Infectious Diseases*, 7th ed. St. Louis: Churchill Livingstone/Harcourt Health Sciences; 2010.

Pickering LK, ed. *2009 Red Book, Report of the Committee on Infectious Diseases*, 28th ed. Elk Grove: American Academy of Pediatrics; 2009.

Porter, RS and Kaplan, JL, eds. *The Merck Manual of Diagnosis and Therapy*, 19th ed. Whitehouse Station: Merck & Company; 2011.

Tortora GJ, Funke BR, Case CL. *Microbiology, An Introduction*, 10th ed. San Francisco: Benjamin Cummings Publishing; 2009.

Versalovic J, Carroll KC, Jorgensen JH, Funke G, Landry ML, Warnock DW, eds. *Manual of Clinical Microbiology*, 12th ed. Washington, DC: American Society of Microbiology Press; 2011.

Additional Resources

APIC Text Online. 2011. http://text.apic.org/

American Society for Microbiology. http://www.asm.org

Centers for Disease Control and Prevention. http://www.cdc.gov

Doctor fungus. http://www.doctorfungus.org

Emerging & Re-emerging Infectious Diseases. In: NIH Education, Understanding Infectious Diseases. Available at http://science.education.nih.gov/supplements/nih1/diseases/guide/understanding1.htm Accessed 1/4/2012.

Fungi as Human Pathogens. In: University of Hawaii, Botany Lecture. Available at http://www.earthtym.net/ref-fungi-path.htm. Accessed 1/17/2012.

Health-care Associated Infections. http://www.cdc.gov/hai/

Micromedex Healthcare Series. www.micromedex.com/products/hcs/

Mycology Online. http://www.mycology.adelaide.edu.au

SHEA Guidelines and Resources. Compendium of Strategies to Prevent HAIs. Available at http://www.shea-online.org/GuidelinesResources/CompendiumofStrategiestoPreventHAIs.aspx

The Sanford Guide to Antimicrobial Therapy 41st edition, 2011. http://www.sanfordguide.com

World Health Organization. http://www.who.int

Chapter Three

Parasites

By definition, a parasite is an organism that lives upon, or within, another organism and, at whose expense, obtains some advantage. If we removed all the viruses and all the parasitic bacteria and fungi from the list of life forms, there would still be a greater number of parasites remaining. There are parasites within nearly every biological grouping from the single-celled protozoa to humans. Humans alone play host to well over a hundred different parasites, some of which we share with other species. Usually when present in low numbers, parasites exist without causing harm or even noticeable sign of their presence. Sometimes they can be the etiology of significant morbidity and mortality.

Growth

Human parasites range in size and complexity from microscopic, intracellular ones and single-cell protozoa to tapeworms of up to 50 feet in length. Most protozoan parasites exist in two different forms or stages:

- Trophozoite stage – feeds, metabolizes, and produces effects in the host characteristic of a disease associated with that organism.
- Cyst stage – essentially dormant, more refractile, and stable in the environment outside of the host and is the stage most responsible for transmission of the parasite between hosts. Other parasites require one or more specific species to host a sexual, asexual, or developmental stage of their complex life cycle. These different hosts might serve as nutritional sources or possibly as vectors to the next host in the cycle.

Taxonomy

The human parasites are classified in three major groups or taxonomic sub-kingdoms:

1. Protozoa are the simplest life forms and include the unicellular amoebae, flagellates, ciliates, and tissue-dwelling organisms that contain no flagella or cilia and reproduce either sexually or asexually. Protozoa that are pathogenic to humans are classified into four groups based on mode

of movement:

- Sarcodina (amoeba), e.g., *Entamoeba*
- Mastigophora (flagellates), e.g., *Giardia, Leishmania*
- Ciliophora (ciliates), e.g., *Balantidium*
- Sporozoa (organisms whose adult stage is not motile, e.g., *Plasmodium, Cryptosporidium*

2. Helminths are large, multicellular organisms whose adult stages are generally visible to the naked eye. Infection is the result of eggs that hatch into larvae in the jejunum and small intestine of humans. In adult form, helminths cannot multiply in humans. Three main groups of helminths (worms) that cause infections in humans are:

- Flat worms (platyhelminths), include trematodes (flukes) and cestodes (tapeworms)
- Thorny-headed worms (acanthocephalins), adult forms reside in gastrointestinal tract
- Roundworms (nematodes), adult forms can reside in gastrointestinal tract, blood, lymphatic system, or subcutaneous tissues. Larval states can also cause infection in various body tissues.

3. Ectoparasites refer to organisms such as ticks, fleas, lice, and mites that attach or burrow into the skin and remain for relatively long periods of time.

Bioterrorism Agents

Parasites that are considered bioterrorism agents are denoted in the following manner: In the "Infections" column, the term **"bioterrorism agent"** is in bold letters, including classification of category A, B, or C. For special considerations regarding bioterrorism agents, refer to the "Bioterrorism Agents" Chapter.

Table

The following table will help guide the user through an understanding of parasites. Note that the table:

- Lists the parasites by Genus
- Provides a description of the parasite as well as reservoirs or where normally found
- Lists the names
- Describes infections and syndromes
- List the mode(s) of transmission

Genus	Description	Name	Infections	Mode(s) of Transmission
Acanthamoeba	free-living amoeba; found in fresh water and soil; worldwide; contaminated water sources (i.e. pools, hot tubs, drinking water systems); sewage systems; air (i.e. cooling towers, heating and air ventilation systems)	A. castellanii A. culbertsoni	cutaneous infections; chronic granulomatous amoebic encephalitis; keratitis due to contaminated contact lens solution; sinusitis; infection of connective tissue around bone; disseminated infection in immunocompromised	contact with contaminated water or soil
Ancylostoma	nematode (roundworm); hookworm; worldwide, prevalent in Asia and Sub-Saharan Africa	A. duodenale	asymptomatic infections; severe infections: anemia, diarrhea, fatigue, weight loss; "ground itch," pruritus, rash at skin penetration site	skin penetration; ingestion
Anisakis	nematode (roundworm); parasites of marine mammals that can also infect humans	A. simplex	accidental infection with larval form and intestinal penetration (most common); gastric penetration and resulting complications	consumption of raw or under-cooked infected fish (e.g. sushi or sashimi)
Ascaris	intestinal nematode (roundworm); worldwide, most common in tropical and subtropical areas; reservoir - humans, pigs	A. lumbricoides	asymptomatic infections; severe infections: impaired digestion or absorption of dietary proteins, cramping, vomiting, obstruction (esp. in children); pulmonary disease	fecal-oral; consumption of food or water containing worm eggs originating from contaminating soil
Babesia	protozoan (single-cell); parasite in blood of cattle that can also infect humans; worldwide; reservoir - deer mice, other small mammals; outbreaks in Northeast, Midwest and West Coast U.S., Europe, and Japan	B. divergens	babesiosis resembles malaria; disease only in splenectomized patients; hemolytic anemia; fever and hepatosplenomegaly; hemoglobinuria and renal insufficiency in severe cases	bite of an infected Ixodes scapularis tick
	protozoan (single-cell); parasite in blood of rodents that can also infect humans	B. microti	resembles malaria; hemolytic anemia; fever and hepatosplenomegaly; hemoglobinuria and renal insufficiency in severe cases; severest cases in splenectomized patients	bite of an infected Ixodes scapularis tick

(continued)

Genus	Description	Name	Infections	Mode(s) of Transmission
Balamuthia	free-living amoeba; found worldwide in soil, possibly fresh water	B. mandrillaris	central nervous system infections; cutaneous infections; rare, often fatal granulomatous amoebic encephalitis	contaminated soil contact with skin wounds and cuts; dust inhalation
Balantidium	intestinal ciliated protozoan (single-cell); parasite of swine that can also infect primates and humans; worldwide	B. coli	invasion of the colon; possible appendicitis or dysenteric syndrome with rectosigmoid ulceration; lower abdominal pain, vomiting, cramping, diarrhea	fecal-oral; associated with infected swine or primates; consumption of food or water contaminated with organism cysts
Blastocystis	intestinal protozoan (single-cell); parasite associated with diarrhea in swine; worldwide; reservoir - humans and animals	B. hominis	recurrent diarrhea with fever, vomiting, intense abdominal discomfort; symptoms more pronounced in immunocompromised	fecal-oral; consumption of food or water containing organism cysts
Brugia	tissue nematode (roundworm) of primates and felines that can also infect humans; tropics and subtropics	B. malayi B. timori	malayan filariasis: acute lymphatic inflammation or obstruction such as hydrocele, elephantiasis (lymphatic filariasis) and chyluria	bite of infected mosquito (various species)
Capillaria	intestinal nematode (roundworm); endemic in Philippines, Thailand; rare cases in other countries	C. philippinensis	relatively rare; capillariasis; abdominal pain, flatulence, intermittent diarrhea, vomiting, weight loss, anorexia, muscle wasting, generalized massive edema	consumption of raw (fresh or brackish water) fish infected with the larval stages
Chilomastix	intestinal flagellated protozoan (single-cell); worldwide	C. mesnili	nonpathogenic; presence may suggest poor living conditions or compromised hygiene	fecal-oral; consumption of food or water containing organism cysts
Chlonorchis	intestinal trematode (fluke); the Oriental or Chinese liver fluke; parasite of fish-eating mammals that can also infect humans; common in Asia	C. sinensis	asymptomatic infections; severe infections: cholangitis, cholangiohepatitis	consumption of infected raw or undercooked fish

Cryptosporidium	intestinal protozoan (single-cell); associated with diarrhea, especially in domesticated livestock; can also infect humans; worldwide; reservoir - humans, cattle; contaminated water (recreational water parks and swimming pools) implicated in outbreaks in developing countries occurs mostly in children under 5 years of age	*C. parvum* *C. hominis*	self-limiting cryptosporidiosis: watery diarrhea with abdominal cramps, fever and nausea; intestinal, biliary, respiratory tract infections; common in immunocompromised, chronic (weeks to years) profuse watery diarrhea in AIDS patients; **Category B bioterrorism agent**	fecal-oral, ingestion of contaminated fruits, vegetables, shellfish, water; direct contact with infected animal or human
Cyclospora	intestinal protozoan (single-cell); worldwide; endemic in Central and South America, Caribbean, Mexico, Indonesia, Asia, Nepal, Africa, India; common in Southern Europe, Middle East	*C. cayetanensis*	often asymptomatic; prolonged, relapsing, watery diarrhea, weight loss; abdominal pain, nausea, vomiting, fever	fecal-oral; associated with consumption of fresh raspberries, strawberries or other fruits and vegetables from Central America
Dientamoeba	intestinal flagellated protozoan (single-cell) having no cyst stage; worldwide; high prevalence in missionaries, native Americans in Arizona, institutionalized persons	*D. fragilis*	diarrheal disease especially in children; nausea, vomiting and weight loss; noninvasive diarrheal illness	fecal-oral; contaminated food or water
Diphyllobothrium	intestinal cestode (tapeworm or segmented worm); the fish tapeworm; longest intestinal parasite of humans; worldwide; common in Scandinavian Lake areas, Northern Europe, North and South America	*D. latum*	asymptomatic infections; severe infections: lead to competition with host for vitamins, such as B12 and folate, resulting in deficiency, megaloblastic anemia and neurologic symptoms	consumption of infected raw or undercooked fish (pikeburbot, perch, ruff, turbot)
Dirofilaria	tissue nematode (roundworm); the dog heartworm which can infect humans; common in Southern U.S. along Gulf and Atlantic coasts, Mississippi River; hosts - dogs, foxes, bears	*D. immitis*	usually asymptomatic; pulmonary dirofilariasis; pulmonary embolism evoking granulomatous response producing "coin lesions," cough, chest pain, hemoptysis	bite of an infected mosquito

(continued)

Genus	Description	Name	Infections	Mode(s) of Transmission
Dracunculus	tissue nematode (guinea worm); found in remote poverty areas of Africa with no safe, drinking water; dry regions, infections occur during the rainy season, when stagnant surface water is available; wet regions, infections occur during the dry season, when surface water becomes stagnant	*D. medinensis*	infected blisters; inflammation, tissue damage, lesions mainly on lower extremities, may occur anywhere in the body	ingestion of unfiltered water from ponds and other stagnant surface water sources
Echinococcus	tissue cestode (tapeworm or segmented worm); the dog tapeworm or hydatid tapeworm; worldwide	*E. granulosus* *E. multilocularis*	hydatid, fluid-filled cysts usually in the liver and/or lungs, other organs as well	ingestion of worm eggs in feces from infected dogs contaminating food or water; hand to mouth from fomites
Endolimax	intestinal amoebic protozoan (single-cell)	*E. nana*	nonpathogenic; presence may suggest poor living conditions or compromised hygiene	fecal-oral; consumption of food or water containing organism cysts
Entamoeba	intestinal amoebic protozoan (single-cell); worldwide, higher prevalence in areas with poor sanitation	*E. coli*	nonpathogenic; presence may suggest poor living conditions or compromised hygiene	fecal-oral; consumption of food or water containing organism cysts
		E. dispar	nonpathogenic; physically indistinguishable from *E. histolytica*	fecal-oral; consumption of food or water containing organism cysts
		E. hartmanni	nonpathogenic; presence may suggest poor living conditions or compromised hygiene	fecal-oral; consumption of food or water containing organism cysts
	worldwide, tropical and subtropical regions; reservoir - humans	*E. histolytica*	colonic irritation; amoebic dysentery; toxic megacolon; amoeboma; chronic irritative bowel syndrome; cutaneous amoebiasis; amoebic liver disease; invasive intestinal and extraintestinal amebiasis	fecal-oral; consumption of food or water containing organism cysts; oral-anal sex

Genus	Description	Species	Clinical Manifestations	Transmission
	associated with pigs; most common intestinal parasite in Papua New Guinea	E. polecki	diarrheal disease; mostly seen in the Orient	fecal-oral; consumption of food or water containing organism cysts
Enterobius	intestinal nematode (roundworm); pinworm; worldwide, more common in children	E. vermicularis	can be asymptomatic; nocturnal perianal pruritus; occasional ectopic disease such as appendicitis, salpingitis, or ulcerative bowel lesions	fecal-oral; consumption of worm eggs via contact with fomites or airborne
Fasciola	intestinal trematode (fluke); the sheep and/or liver or common liver fluke; worldwide	F. hepatica	liver enlargement; bile duct obstruction; biliary cirrhosis	consumption of plants or food contaminated with soil containing infective forms
Fasciolopsis	intestinal fluke; the large intestinal or giant fluke; primarily in Southeast Asia	F. buski	mostly asymptomatic; severe infections: diarrhea, abdominal pain and malabsorption	consumption of plants or food contaminated with soil containing infective forms
Giardia	intestinal flagellated protozoan (single-cell); worldwide; reservoir - human and many animal species; most common cause of intestinal parasitosis worldwide; common in developing countries, day care centers, immunocompromised, hikers	G. intestinalis G. lamblia G. duodenalis	giardiasis can be asymptomatic; travelers' diarrhea; acute diarrhea, abdominal cramps, bloating, flatulence; may become chronic; "failure to thrive" in children	fecal-oral; consumption of cysts in contaminated water or food; inoculum of only 10-100 cysts sufficient for infection
Gnathostoma	intestinal nematode; most commonly found in Southeast Asia, South and Central America, and in some areas of Africa; hosts = variety of mammals	G. doloresi G. nipponicum G. hispidum G. spingerum	dermatologic manifestations of gnathostomiasis; panniculitis, creeping eruptions, pseudofurunculosis; eye involvement may result in vision loss or blindness; CNS involvement may result in nerve pain, paralysis, coma and death; any visceral organ may be affected; considered a subtype of visceral larval migrans	ingestion of raw or undercooked fresh water fish, eels, frogs, birds, and reptiles

(continued)

Genus	Description	Name	Infections	Mode(s) of Transmission
Hymenolepis	intestinal cestode (tapeworm or segmented worm); smallest intestinal tapeworm of humans; a parasite of mice; most common tapeworm that can infect humans; worldwide	*H. nana* aka Dwarf Tapeworm *H. diminuta* aka Rat Tapeworm	can be asymptomatic; abdominal cramps; diarrhea; severe infections: neurotoxic worm products lead to dizziness and seizures; possible autoinfection	consumption of worm eggs; hatching larvae from eggs of infecting worms (autoinfection)
Isospora	intestinal protozoan (single-cell); worldwide, mainly tropical and subtropical areas	*I. belli*	can be asymptomatic; watery diarrhea, abdominal cramps, flatulence, nausea, vomiting, signs of malabsorption; severe in infants and young children; frequent, severe and sometimes fatal in immunocompromised patients	fecal-oral; consumption of food or water contaminated with organism cysts
Leishmania	tissue protozoan (single-cell) of small carnivores that can infect humans; worldwide; reservoir - humans, many animal species, including wild and domestic foxes, dogs, some marsupials	*L. braziliensis* *L. major*	cutaneous disease (majority of leishmaniasis in Afghanistan, Algeria, Iran, Iraq, Saudi Arabia, Syria) with chronic, latent, and metastatic mucosal membrane involvement; mucocutaneous disease (mainly Bolivia, Brazil, Peru); opportunistic in immunocompromised	sand fly bite
		L. donovani	visceral disease; "kalaazar" (black fever) in India: subacute or chronic course with fever, hepatosplenomegaly, anemia, progressive emaciation	sand fly bite
		L. mexicana	cutaneous disease resembling that caused by *L. tropica*	sand fly bite
		L. tropica	"oriental sore:" cutaneous disease seen in tropical and subtropical Africa and Asia; resembles syphilis, leprosy or cutaneous tuberculosis	sand fly bite
Loa	tissue nematode (African Eye roundworm); rain forests of West and Central Africa	*L. loa*	infections of the subconjunctiva; migration through connective tissues; subcutaneous edema called "Calabar swellings" around wrist or knee joints	*Tabanid* flies (deer flies)

Naegleria	free-living amoeba found worldwide in fresh water, sewage, sludge, and soil	*N. fowleri*	acute and fulminating primary amoebic meningoencephalitis (rare, severe brain infection)	contaminated water from small fresh water lakes or swimming pools forced under pressure (during swimming, diving, or skiing) through the nasal mucosa covering the cribriform plate to the meninges
Necator	nematode (roundworm); hookworm; worldwide	*N. americanus*	asymptomatic infections; severe infections: anemia, diarrhea, fatigue, weight loss; "ground itch," pruritus, rash at skin penetration site	skin penetration
Onchocerca	tissue nematode (roundworm); tropical areas - equatorial Africa, Saharan, Yemen, Central and South America	*O. volvulus*	infections involve nodules under the skin or debilitating itching, lymph nodes, eyes; River blindness; worldwide onchocerciasis is second only to trachoma as an infectious cause of blindness	black fly bite
Paragonimus	tissue trematode (fluke); Oriental lung fluke (eggs found in sputum); worldwide, common in China, Southeast Asia	*P. westermani*	asymptomatic infections; chest pain, hemoptysis, chronic bronchitis or bronchiectasis, pleuritic chest pain, lung abscess	consumption of infected crawfish or freshwater crab
Parastrongylus	tissue nematode (roundworm); worldwide; public health threat in Southeast Asia and Asian Pacific Islands; host - variety of rodents	*P. cantonensis*	meningitis; meningoencephalitis; eye with retinal detachment and blindness; pulmonary disease	ingestion of infected mollusk or infected paratenic hosts (i.e. shrimp, crabs, fish, frogs)
Plasmodium	tissue protozoan (single-cell); tropical and subtropical areas; reservoir - humans, possibly other primates	*P. falciparum*	malignant malaria: anemia, undulating high fever, chills, acute renal failure, cerebral dysfunction	infected Anopheles mosquito bite; transfusion with infected blood
		P. malariae *P. ovale* *P. vivax*	malaria: similar to disease caused by *P. falciparum* but less severe	infected Anopheles mosquito bite; transfusion with infected blood

(continued)

Genus	Description	Name	Infections	Mode(s) of Transmission
		P. knowlesi	malaria seen in Southeast Asia; host - infected pigtailed macaques	infected Anopheles mosquito bite
Schistosoma	tissue trematode (fluke); the blood or snail flukes; eggs found in stool; common in tropical regions; snail - intermediate host		intestinal schistosomiasis	penetration of infectious worm stage through skin
	eggs found in urine; common in Africa	S. haematobium	genitourinary schistosomiasis	penetration of infectious worm stage through skin
	eggs found in stool; common in Indonesia, China, Philippines; S. mekong found in Laos and Cambodia	S. japonicum S. mekongi	same as for S. mansoni; acute disease more pronounced due to heavy egg production; egg embolism possible in chronic disease	penetration of infectious worm stage through skin
	common in Africa, Caribbean, South America	S. mansoni	dermatitis ("swimmer's itch") at worm entry through skin; acute schistosomiasis (Katayama fever): serum sickness-like syndrome; chronic disease	penetration of infectious worm stage through skin
	common in Africa	S. intercalatum	rectal schistosomiasis	penetration of infectious worm stage through skin
Strongyloides	intestinal nematode (roundworm); mainly tropical and subtropical areas in warm moist soil	S. stercoralis	chronic infections; strongyloidiasis can be asymptomatic; burning or colicky abdominal pain with diarrhea and mucus, nausea, vomiting, weight loss; lethal autoinfection in immunocompromised	penetration of infectious worm stage through skin; hatching larvae from eggs of infecting worms (autoinfection)
Taenia	intestinal cestode (tapeworm or segmented worm); the beef tapeworm; worldwide	T. saginata	can be asymptomatic; diarrhea; abdominal cramps; rare intestinal obstruction	consumption of raw or under-cooked infected beef

	Description	Species	Disease	Transmission
	the pork tapeworm; endemic in all parts of developing world where pigs are raised	*T. solium*	same as for *T. saginata*; neuro-cysticercosis: worms encysted in almost any tissue if eggs are consumed	consumption of raw or undercooked infected pork; ingestion of worm eggs
Toxocara	tissue nematode (round worm); found worldwide in soil; among most common helminthic infections; higher infection rates among people living in poverty	*T. canis* / *T. cati*	subclinical; severe forms involve eyes, heart, brain, or other vital organs; toxocariasis in pregnant woman may result in miscarriage	direct contact with contaminated soil or sand (sandbox) infected feces of dogs (*T. canis*) and/or cats (*T. cati*); ingestion of raw or undercooked meat (raw lamb or calf's liver)
Toxoplasma	obligate intracellular protozoan (single-cell); parasite of animals that can also infect humans; one of the most common parasitic infections; worldwide; cats - important reservoir become infected after eating small animals and birds	*T. gondii*	toxoplasmosis: asymptomatic or mild disease; chronic or latent: tissue cysts in brain, heart, skeletal muscle; encephalitis, myocarditis, pneumonitis in immunocompromised; birth defects and/or serious infections in infants of mothers becoming infected during last trimester; chorioretinitis	major modes: oral and congenital; consumption of tissue cysts in under cooked, contaminated meat; consumption of infectious forms originating from cat feces; organ transplantation; blood transfusion; transplacental transmission
Trichinella	tissue nematode (roundworm); worldwide	*T. spiralis*	asymptomatic; trichinosis: encysted worm larvae in skeletal muscle; early disease: diarrhea, abdominal pain, vomiting; late disease: fever, periorbital edema, myositis, weakness	consumption of raw or undercooked infected pork
Trichomonas	tissue flagellated protozoan (single-cell) having no cyst stage; worldwide	*T. vaginalis*	vaginal and exocervical inflammation with hemorrhage, ulceration, and foul-smelling discharge; often as co-pathogen with other venereal disease agents; presence in minors may suggest abuse; urethritis in males; neonatal pneumonia	sexually transmitted; genital secretions via fomites

(continued)

Genus	Name	Infections	Mode(s) of Transmission
Trichuris — intestinal nematode (roundworm); the whipworm; worldwide, most associated with children in tropical and subtropical regions	*T. trichiura*	asymptomatic; severe infections: mild anemia, bloody stools and possible rectal prolapse; children with serious infection may develop growth retardation due to chronic malnutrition and anemia	consumption of worm eggs
Trypanosoma — tissue protozoan (single-cell) of small carnivores that can infect humans; reservoir - humans, possibly domestic and wild animals	*T. brucei gambiense*	West African (Gambian) trypanosomiasis: sleeping sickness, systemic inflammation due to build up of immune complexes; chronic illness; primarily confined to Africa	bite of tsetse fly
	T. brucei rhodesiense	East African (Rhodesian) trypanosomiasis: same as West African but more severe and with rash; acute morbidity and mortality; primarily confined to Central Africa	bite of tsetse fly
confined to American continent (Central and South America, California, Louisiana, Texas)	*T. cruzi*	American trypanosomiasis (Chagas' disease): periocular edema (Romana's sign), fever, anorexia, edema of face and lower extremities; severe myocarditis	feces of reduviid bug scratched into skin; blood transfusion; organ transplantation; congenital
host-animals (buffalo, camels, cattle, horses, rats); wide geographical region – Africa, Asia, Central and South America	*T. evansi*	transient fevers, sensory disorders	transmitted by bloodsucking insects (i.e. stable flies or horse flies)
reservoir - animals, dogs, cats, armadillo, raccoons, rodents, opossums	*T. rangeli*	asymptomatic infection; present only on American continent	tsetse fly
Wuchereria — tissue nematode (roundworm); tropics and subtropics; reservoir - humans	*W. bancrofti*	bancroftian filariasis: acute lymphatic inflammation or obstruction such as hydrocele, elephantiasis (lymphatic filariasis); and chyluria	bite of infected mosquito (varied species)

References

Brooks GF, Butel JS, Morse SA. *Jawetz, Melnick, & Adelberg's Medical Microbiology*. 24th ed. New York: Appleton-Lange Medical Books/McGraw-Hill; 2010.

Forbes B, Sahm DF, Weissfeld AS. *Bailey & Scott's Diagnostic Microbiology*. 12th ed. St. Louis: Mosby-Yearbook/Harcourt Health Sciences; 2007.

Gilbert DN, Moellering RC, Eliopoulos GM, Chambers HF, Saag MS. *The Sanford Guide to Antimicrobial Therapy 2011*. 41st ed. Sperryville, VA: Antimicrobial Therapy, Inc.; 2011.

Grota P, ed. *APIC Text of Infection Control and Epidemiology*, 4th ed. Washington, DC: Association for Professionals in Infection Control and Epidemiology, 2014.

Heymann DL, ed. *Control of Communicable Diseases Manual*, 19th ed. Baltimore: American Public Health Association, United Book Press, Inc.; 2008.

Mahon CR, Lehman, DC, Manuselis G, eds. *Textbook of Diagnostic Microbiology*, 4th ed. St. Louis: W.B. Saunders Company/Harcourt Health Sciences; 2010.

Mandell GL, Bennett JE, Dolin R, eds. *Principles and Practice of Infectious Diseases*, 7th ed. St. Louis: Churchill Livingstone/Harcourt Health Sciences; 2010.

Pickering LK, ed. *2009 Red Book, Report of the Committee on Infectious Diseases*, 28th ed. Elk Grove: American Academy of Pediatrics; 2009.

Porter, RS and Kaplan, JL, eds. *The Merck Manual of Diagnosis and Therapy*, 19th ed. Whitehouse Station: Merck & Company; 2011.

Roberts LS, Janovy J, Schmidt GD. *Foundations of Parasitology*, 8th ed. McGraw-Hill Higher Education Publishing; 2009.

Tortora GJ, Funke BR, Case CL. *Microbiology, An Introduction*, 10th ed. San Francisco: Benjamin Cummings Publishing; 2009.

Versalovic J, Carroll KC, Jorgensen JH, Funke G, Landry ML, Warnock DW, eds. *Manual of Clinical Microbiology*, 12th ed. Washington, DC: American Society of Microbiology Press; 2011.

Additional Resources

APIC Text Online. 2011. http://text.apic.org/

American Society for Microbiology. http://www.asm.org

Centers for Disease Control and Prevention. http://www.cdc.gov

CDC Emerging Human Infections Diseases: Anthroponoses, Zoonoses, and Sapronoses. In: Appendix: Important Anthroponoses, Zoonoses, and Sapronoses. Available at http://wwwnc.cdc.gov/eid/article/9/3/02-0208_article.htm. Accessed 7/26/2010.

Emerging & Re-emerging Infectious Diseases. In: NIH Education, Understanding Infectious Diseases. Available at http://science.education.nih.gov/supplements/nih1/diseases/guide/understanding1.htm. Accessed 1/4/2012.

Health-care Associated Infections. http://www.cdc.gov/hai/

Micromedex Healthcare Series. www.micromedex.com/products/hcs/

Parasites. In: CDC About Parasites. Available at http://www.cdc.gov/parasites/about.html. Accessed 2/7/2012.

Parasitic Infections in Humans. In: New England BioLabs. Available at http://www.neb.com/nebecomm/tech_reference/protein_tools/paracitic_infections_in_humans.asp. Accessed 2/7/2012.

SHEA Guidelines and Resources. Compendium of Strategies to Prevent HAIs. Available at http://www.shea-online.org/GuidelinesResources/CompendiumofStrategiestoPreventHAIs.aspx

The Sanford Guide to Antimicrobial Therapy 41st edition, 2011. http://www.sanfordguide.com

World Health Organization. http://www.who.int

Chapter Four

Viruses

Viral agents play a major role in infectious diseases throughout the world, affecting humans as well as plants and other animals.

Growth

Viruses are obligate intracellular parasites that require living host cells to grow and reproduce. Intact viral particles, called virions, are made up of nucleic acid (either RNA or DNA) and a protein coat (capsid) and possibly an envelope composed of viral proteins and host cell lipid. They are taken in by living host cells where they modify the cell metabolism to produce new nucleic acid and protein coat. The virus particles are assembled and released by the cell to invade other host cells. The release process may cause host cell damage that leads to pathology and signs and symptoms of infection. Some viruses will lie dormant in the host cell for months or years. After this latent period, the virus forms new virus particles and damages the host cell.

Taxonomy

The nomenclature of viral agents appears to be more confusing and less standardized than that of bacteria, fungi, and parasites. Instead of genus and species names, viruses are often referred to by "common names" derived from the organ system involved (e.g., Hand, Foot, and Mouth Disease), the disease produced (e.g., Hepatitis Virus), or the location in which the disease was first seen (Norwalk Virus). The taxonomy of the viruses is generally based on:

- Whether the virus contains DNA or RNA
- The size and shape of the virus
- The structure of the protein coat
- The presence or absence of an envelope
- The mode of replication

Vaccines

Since viral particles contain protein coats that possess "good" antigens, viruses are often made into safe and efficacious vaccines. Virus vaccines are either live attenuated vaccines that are "weakened" from their wild types or inactivated vaccines that are heated or chemically treated. Vaccines for prevention of viral diseases include: poliomyelitis, measles, mumps, rubella, varicella, hepatitis A, hepatitis B, and influenza.

Bioterrorism Agents

Viruses that are considered bioterrorism agents are denoted in the following manner: In the "Infections" column, the term **"bioterrorism agent"** is in bold letters, including classification of category A, B, or C. For special considerations regarding bioterrorism agents, refer to the "Bioterrorism Agents" Chapter.

Pandemic Influenza Concerns

Influenza: Three types – A, B, C

- Type A Virus and Subtypes: Influenza type A viruses can infect people, birds, pigs, horses, dogs, marine mammals, and other animals. Subtypes are based on two proteins on the surface of the virus: hemagglutinin (HA) and neuraminidase (NA). For example, H5N1, Avian flu, contains 5 HA proteins and 1NA protein on the virus surface. There are 16 known HA subtypes and 9 known NA subtypes. Influenza A viruses have been the predominant cause of worldwide pandemics. In 2009, influenza H1N1 virus with swine, avian and human genes (antigenic shift) caused the first pandemic in more than 40 years.
- Type B Virus can result in epidemics with mild clinical illnesses compared to Type A influenza.
- Type C Virus has not been associated with large epidemics and is less common than Types A and B. Clinical illness is much like the common cold.

Table

The following table will help guide the user through an understanding of viruses. Note that the table:

- Lists the virus by common name(s) and other associated names (also know as), **("Name + AKA")**, if applicable
- Provides a description (RNA or DNA genome) as well as reservoirs and geographic distribution
- Lists family and genus
- Describes infections and syndromes, transmission, incubation, and vaccines, if applicable

Name + (AKA)	Description	Family/Genus	Infections and Syndromes	Transmission and Incubation
Adenovirus	DNA genomes; approximately 52 human adenovirus types; Types 1, 2, 3, and 5 most common; reservoir: humans, water, fomites (e.g. ophthalmological equipment/solutions), environment; worldwide distribution	Adenoviridae/Mastadenovirus	acute febrile respiratory disease in children; Types 1, 2, 5 results in latency of virus in the tonsils and adenoids, fever with or without pharyngitis, tracheitis, bronchitis, moderately persistent nonproductive cough; an increase in primary infection seen in immunocompromised individuals and immunocompromised individuals shed the virus longer.	direct and indirect contact; fecal-oral; incubation: 1–10 days
	Types 3 and 7; (Type 3 more prevalent during cold weather)		meningitis; pharyngoconjunctival fever: conjunctivitis initially unilateral with pain, pharyngitis and lower respiratory tract involvement with cough; illness subsides within 7 days; follicular conjunctivitis may persist up to 10 days	direct and indirect contact; incubation: 5–10 days; oral vaccine (Type 7) available for military
	Type 4: epidemic in military recruits; primarily affects adults; epidemics of pneumonia in children		acute respiratory disease (ARD): malaise, chills, fever, headache; nasopharyngitis, hoarseness, dry cough; follicular conjunctivitis	direct and indirect contact; incubation up to 10 days; oral vaccine available for military
	Type 8: epidemic in adults; widespread in Japan; rare in U.S.		epidemic keratoconjunctivitis; sudden onset one eye initially red followed by periorbital swelling, preauricular lymphadenopathy, superficial corneal opacities, local pain (foreign body-like irritation); other eye may become involved within 1 week; usually lasts 3–4 weeks	direct and indirect contact; incubation: 5–12 days or more
	Type 11: infants and immunocompromised persons at greatest risk		acute hemorrhagic cystitis: urinary frequency, bladder pain, gross or microscopic hematuria, minimal pyuria, viremia; follicular conjunctivitis	direct and indirect contact
	Types 40 and 41: primarily affects <2y/o; outbreaks in orphanages, hospitals, daycare centers		gastroenteritis (enteric adenovirus): watery diarrhea 6–9 days with range of 4–23 days; vomiting, fever may precede or accompany diarrhea	fecal-oral; incubation: 3–10 days

(continued)

Name + (AKA)	Description	Family/Genus	Infections and Syndromes	Transmission and Incubation
BK virus (BKV)	DNA genome; human reservoir; worldwide distribution	Papovaviridae – Polyomavirus	infections are asymptomatic or minimally symptomatic; mild upper respiratory tract symptoms; occur mostly in immunocompromised adults; rare cases of Progressive multifocal leukoencephalopathy (PML); Polyomavirus-associated nephropathy; hemorrhagic cystitis; urethral stenosis; and hematuria; potential cause of cancer	little is known about transmission or events during primary infection; no definitive evidence of perinatal transmission with maternal viruria
Borna virus	RNA genome: reservoir: rodents; worldwide distribution	Bornaviridae – Bornavirus	neuropsychiatric disorders	secretions; incubation: variable
California encephalitis virus (Arbovirus)	RNA genome; reservoir: *Aedes* mosquito egg	Bunyaviridae – Bunyavirus	encephalitis	infected mosquito bite; incubation: usually 5–15 days
Colorado tick fever virus (CTF)	RNA genome; reservoir: Wood tick	Reoviridae – Coltivirus	sudden onset of saddleback" fever: retro-orbital pain, myalgia of legs and back and leukopenia	bite of infected tick; incubation: four days
Coronavirus	RNA genome; reservoir; humans	Coronaviridae – Coronavirus	common cold; rare pneumonia and bronchitis; gastroenteritis	aerosol of respiratory secretions; incubation: 2–5 days
	RNA genome; reservoir: bats; major outbreaks: Canada, China, Singapore, Viet Nam	SARS – associated coronavirus (SARS-CoV)	SARS (Severe Acute Respiratory Syndrome): severe lower respiratory illness, fever, chills, rigors, myalgia, headache, shortness of breath, dry cough	direct contact; respiratory droplets, indirect contact with fomites (contaminated surfaces or objects); incubation: 2–10 days (mean 5 days)
Cowpox virus	DNA genome; reservoir: humans, cats, cattle, rodents	Poxviridae/ Chordopoxvirinae – Orthopoxvirus	fever and flu-like symptoms; painful papules evolve to crusts, usually located on hands or face; cutaneous lesions heal in 3–4 weeks, up to 12 weeks with scarring common	infected animals usually cats; incubation: 7 days
Coxsackievirus	RNA genomes; group A: serotypes 1-24; reservoir: humans; worldwide distribution; frequent outbreaks in childcare centers	Picornaviridae – Enterovirus	febrile illness, aseptic meningitis, encephalitis, herpangina (vesicular pharyngitis A2-6, 8, 10, 22), hand-foot-mouth disease (vesicular stomatitis-A5, 7, 9, 10, 16); lymphonodular pharyngitis (A10); epidemic hemorrhagic conjunctivitis (A24); exanthems	direct contact with secretions; fecal-oral; inhalation of aerosols; incubation: 3–5 days

Virus	Family	Clinical features	Transmission / Incubation
(continued) RNA genomes; group B: serotypes 1-6; reservoir: humans; worldwide distribution; frequent outbreaks in childcare centers		pleurodynia (Bornholm disease), Devil's grip, pericarditis, myocarditis, generalized disease of the newborn, aseptic meningitis	direct contact with secretions; fecal-oral; inhalation of aerosols; incubation: 3–5 days
Crimean-Congo hemorrhagic fever (Central Asian hemorrhagic fever; Congo fever) — RNA genome; Eastern Europe; Mediterranean, northwestern China, central Asia, southern Europe, Africa, Middle East; Indian subcontinent	Bunyaviruses	sudden severe headache, chills, fever, vomiting and pain in lower back and upper abdomen muscles; petechial hemorrhages seen 3–5 days after symptoms appear; **Category C bioterrorism agent**	bites of hard-bodied *ixodid* ticks; infected animal blood; improper sterilization of medical equipment, reuse of needles, contamination of medical supplies; incubation: 2–7 days
Cytomegalovirus (CMV, human herpesvirus 5) — DNA genome; reservoir: humans; worldwide distribution	Herpesviridae/ Betaherpesvirinae – Cytomegalovirus	infectious mononucleosis syndrome, congenital cytomegalic inclusion disease, retinitis; associated with hepatitis, pneumonitis, encephalitis, colitis, meningoencephalitis, myocarditis, interstitial pneumonitis, Guillain-Barre syndrome; in HIV: retinitis, polyradiculopathy, mononeuritis multiplex, peripheral neuropathy, esophagitis, colitis, pancreatitis, cholecystitis	perinatal; blood products and post-open heart surgery; intimate exposure by mucosal contact with infected tissues, excretions, and secretions (excreted in urine, saliva, breast milk, cervical secretions, and semen); incubation: 3–8 weeks post transfusion or transplant; and 3–12 weeks post delivery
Dengue virus (dengue hemorrhagic fever (DHF), dengue shock syndrome (DSS), breakbone fever, dandy fever, seven-day fever) — RNA genomes; serotypes 1–4; reservoir: man (possibly monkeys in West Africa and Southeast Asia); severe and fatal disease in children under 15 years of age	Flaviviridae – Flavivirus	sudden onset of fever, severe headache, retro-orbital pain, anorexia, nausea, vomiting, and rash myalgias, and arthralgias, leukopenia, thrombocytopenia, and hemorrhagic manifestations	mosquito (*Aedes aegypti/albopictus*); incubation: 3–10 days
Eastern equine encephalitis virus (EEEV) — RNA genome; reservoir: birds, bats, possibly rodents and *Aedes* mosquitoes; widely distributed in the Americas	Togaviridae – Alphavirus	fever, headache, irritability, restlessness, drowsiness, anorexia, vomiting, diarrhea, cyanosis, convulsions, and coma; encephalomyelitis; **Category B bioterrorism agent**	mosquito bite; incubation: 5–15 days

(continued)

Name + (AKA)	Description	Family/Genus	Infections and Syndromes	Transmission and Incubation
Ebola virus (African hemorrhagic fever, ebola disease, ebola hemorrhagic fever)	RNA genome; reservoir: bats suspected; antibodies found in domestic guinea pigs; distribution: Sudan, Zaire, Ivory Coast, Gabon	Filoviridae – Filovirus	acute infection: sudden onset with high fever, malaise, myalgias, vomiting, diarrhea, maculopapular rash, renal/hepatic involvement and hemorrhagic diathesis; involvement of liver, pancreas, kidney, and to a much less degree the CNS and heart; **Category A bioterrorism agent**	direct contact with infected blood, secretions, organs or semen; aerosols; contaminated syringes and needles; incubation: 2–21 days
Echovirus	RNA genomes; serotypes 1–34; E = enteric C = cytopathic H = human O = orphan reservoir: humans; worldwide distribution	Picornaviridae – Enterovirus	aseptic meningitis, muscle weakness and paralysis, pericarditis, myocarditis, common cold, conjunctivitis, infantile diarrheas, and exanthems, neonatal diarrhea, chronic meningitis	fecal-oral; person to person; incubation: 2–14 days
Enterovirus (new Enteroviruses)	RNA genomes; serotypes 68–71; reservoir: humans; worldwide distribution; outbreaks in eye clinics and tropical areas	Picornaviridae – Enterovirus	acute hemorrhagic conjunctivitis (Enterovirus 70); aseptic meningitis, respiratory illness, encephalitis, hand-foot-mouth disease (rare-Enterovirus 71); myopathy, exanthems	person to person by direct contact; fomites; incubation: 12 hours to 3 days
Epstein-Barr virus (EBV, human herpesvirus 4, kissing disease)	DNA genome; reservoir: humans; worldwide distribution	Herpesviridae/ Gammaherpes-virinae – Lymphocryptovirus	infectious mononucleosis, hepatitis, pneumonitis, myopericarditis, encephalitis, myelitis; associated with chronic fatigue syndrome, African-type Burkitt's lymphoma, nasopharyngeal carcinoma, CNS, and other lymphomas, leiomyosarcoma; in HIV patients: interstitial pneumonia, hairy leukoplakia, B-cell tumors	person to person spread by oropharyngeal route via saliva (frequently by kissing in young persons); blood products; after open heart surgery; perinatal; incubation: 4–6 weeks; for additional resources please visit http://www.cdc.gov/ncidod/diseases/ebv.htm

Hantavirus (hantavirus hemorrhagic fever, Hantaan-Korean hemorrhagic fever, hantavirus respiratory distress syndrome, Four Corners virus)	RNA genome; reservoir: rodents	Bunyaviridae – Hantavirus	hemorrhagic fever with renal syndrome; hantavirus pulmonary syndrome; **Category C bioterrorism agent**	transmission: inhalation of aerosolized rodent urine and feces; incubation: usually 5–15 days
Hepatitis A virus (Enterovirus 72, HAV, infectious hepatitis)	RNA genome; reservoir: humans, chimpanzees (rare); worldwide distribution with sporadic and epidemic cycles	Picornaviridae – Hepatovirus	hepatitis A: fever, malaise, anorexia, nausea, abdominal pain, jaundice	fecal-oral; contaminated food (oysters) and water; blood transfusions (very rare); direct transmission among men who have sex with men; incubation: 15–50 days (dose related)
Hepatitis B virus (HBV, serum hepatitis)	DNA genome; reservoir: humans; worldwide distribution	Hepadnaviridae – Hepadnavirus	primary hepatitis B infection: anorexia, abdominal discomfort, nausea and vomiting, arthalgias, rash, jaundice; can result in chronic HBsAg carrier state; leads to hepatocellular carcinoma and cirrhosis	intimate contact; body excretions and secretions (e.g. blood/serum derived fluids, saliva, semen, and vaginal fluids); percutaneous and permucosal exposure; indirect contact with contaminated inanimate surface (non-intact skin; sharing of shaving razors or toothbrushes); blood products; perinatal transmission; incubation: 45–180 days (usually 60–90)

(continued)

Name + (AKA)	Description	Family/Genus	Infections and Syndromes	Transmission and Incubation
Hepatitis C virus (HCV)	RNA genome; reservoir: humans; worldwide distribution (originally called non-A, non-B hepatitis)	Flaviviridae – Hepacivirus	initial, acute hepatitis C infection: anorexia, abdominal discomfort, nausea and vomiting; leads to chronic infection, hepatocellular carcinoma, cirrhosis	percutaneous; parenteral; sexual contact; incubation: 2 weeks to 6 months
Hepatitis D virus (HDV, delta hepatitis, hepatitis delta virus, delta agent hepatitis, delta associated hepatitis)	defective RNA genome; requires co-infection (HBV) for viral replication; reservoir: humans; worldwide distribution	Hepadnaviridae – Deltavirus	acute infection: only in persons with acute or chronic HBV; onset is abrupt with symptoms resembling HBV; may be self-limiting or progress to chronic hepatitis; coinfection or superinfection; can convert asymptomatic or mild chronic HBV infection into fulminant, severe, or rapidly progressive disease	exposure to blood and serous body fluids; contaminated needles, syringes, and plasma derivatives; sexual transmission; transmission from mother to newborn; incubation: 2–12 weeks, shorter in HBV carriers
Hepatitis E virus (HEV, enterically-transmitted non-A non-B hepatitis [ET-NANB], epidemic non-A non-B hepatitis)	RNA genome; reservoir: unknown; found primarily in countries with inadequate sanitation	Hepeviridae – Hepavirus (reclassified from Caliciviridae – Calicivirus)	acute infection: abrupt onset fever, malaise, anorexia, nausea, abdominal discomfort; followed in a few days by jaundice	fecal-oral; ingestion of contaminated food and water; incubation: 3–8 weeks
Herpes B virus (B virus, herpesvirus simiae, cercopithicine herpesvirus 1, simian virus)	DNA genome; alphaherpesvirus related to HSV; reservoir: Asian monkeys (rhcus and cynomolgus)	Herpesviridae/ Alphaherpesvirinae – Simplexvirus	myelitis; hemorrhagic encephalitis; highly fatal	monkey handlers usually acquire infection from bites and scratches
Herpes simplex virus (HSV)	DNA genome; Types 1 and 2; reservoir: humans; worldwide distribution	Herpesviridae/ Alphaherpesvirinae – Simplexvirus	gingivostomatitis; pharyngitis; herpes labialis; keratoconjunctivitis; encephalitis; cutaneous and genital lesions; esophagitis; pneumonitis; hepatitis; neonatal infection; retinitis; myelitis; erythema multiforme; urethritis; endometritis; salpingitis; prostatitis; proctitis; herpetic whitlow; herpes gladiatorum	perinatal; close contact (mucosal surfaces or openings in skin) with a person shedding virus from a peripheral site, mucosal surface; or in genital or oral secretions; autoinoculation; incubation: 2–12 days
Human herpesvirus (roseola infantum, sixth disease, HHV-6)	DNA genome; Type 6; clinical relevance still being defined; reservoir: humans	Herpesviridae/ Betaherpesvirinae – Roseolovirus	exanthem subitum: maculopapular rash, high fevers, hepatitis; encephalitis	saliva; infects nearly all humans by age 5; incubation: 5–15 days

Human herpesvirus 7 (roseola infantum, HHV-7)	DNA genome; Type 7; reservoir: humans	Herpesviridae/Betaherpesvirinae – Roseolovirus	causes 5% roseola cases (typically milder than HHV-6): fever and maculopapular rash; childhood febrile illnesses	saliva; incubation: unknown; occurs after primary infection with HHV-6
Human herpesvirus 8 (Kaposi's sarcoma)	DNA genome; Type 8; similar to EBV; reservoir: humans	Herpesviridae – Gammaherpesvirises	Kaposi's sarcoma: skin lesions and tumors; multicentric Castleman's disease; primary effusion lymphoma	likely sexually transmitted; virus isolated in saliva, semen, leukocytes
Human immunodeficiency virus (HIV/AIDS)	RNA genome; reservoir: humans; worldwide distribution	Retroviridae/Lentivirinae – Lentivirus	HIV/AIDS; HIV-2: a related disease syndrome primarily in West Africa	sexual contact with or exposure to blood and body fluids; incubation: variable, generally 1–3 months
Human papillomavirus (HPV)	DNA genome; reservoir: humans; worldwide distribution	Papovaviridae – Alphapapillomavirus	infects cutaneous and mucosal epithelium of skin, oral cavity, conjunctive, anus, genital tract; HPV16 and 18 most common types in invasive cancers; HPV6 associated with verrucous carcinoma; cutaneous warts (deep plantar, common, plane, or flat warts); epidermodysplasia verruciformis may resemble flat warts or lesions of pityriasis versicolor covering the torso and upper extremities; anogenital warts are flesh- to gray-colored, hyperkeratotic, exophytic papules; may indicate the existence of cervical HPV squamous epithelial lesions including cervical intraepithelial neoplasia (CIN); infection of the vulva may appear as white patches; most are asymptomatic, frequent itching and burning, pain and tenderness; recurrent respiratory papillomatosis causes hoarseness, respiratory distress; may spread to trachea and lungs	close personal contact; anogenital warts are sexually transmitted; recurrent respiratory papillomatosis in young children acquired by passage through an infected birth canal or in utero; in adults associated with a high number of sexual partners and with oral-genital contact; incubation 2–3 months (range 1–20 months); HPV vaccine now available
Human parvovirus B19 (slapped cheek disease, Fifth disease)	smallest DNA genome; reservoir: humans; worldwide distribution, temperate climates	Parvoviridae - Erythrovirus	erythema infectiosum: rash, arthropathy, aplastic crisis, hydrops fetalis; common in young children	droplet; congenital; blood transfusions from viremic donor (rare); incubation: 4–20 days

(continued)

Name + (AKA)	Description	Family/Genus	Infections and Syndromes	Transmission and Incubation
Human T-cell lympho-tropic virus (HTLV)	RNA genome; Types 1, 2 (3, 4 recently identified); reservoir: infected humans	Retroviridae/ Deltaretrovirus	HTLV 1:T-cell lymphomas and leukemias; HTLV associated myelopathy/tropical spastic paraparesis; HTLV 2 rarely associated with neurological disease	breast milk; sexual contact; IV drug use; transplants; transfusions
Influenza virus	RNA genomes; Types A, B, and C; type A reservoir: humans, swine, equine, avian, and marine mammals; type B reservoir: humans; type C reservoir: humans, swine; worldwide distribution	Orthomyxoviridae – Influenza virus	systemic symptoms: fever/chills, headache, myalgia, malaise, anorexia; respiratory symptoms: dry cough, severe pharyngeal pain, nasal obstruction, discharge; type A: large pandemics with significant mortality in young people; type B: severe disease in the elderly, no pandemics; type C: mild disease without seasonality	aerosol droplets; person-to-person; direct contact; indirect contact with articles recently contaminated by infective nasopharyngeal secretions; annual influenza vaccine consists of 3 inactivated virus strains (2 type A and 1 type B); abrupt onset of symptoms within 1–2 days of infection
Influenza A/H1N1 virus (Swine flu)	RNA genomes; Type A; reservoir: swine	Orthomyxoviridae – Influenza virus	significant febrile respiratory illnesses; **Category C bioterrorism agent**	aerosol droplets; person-to-person; direct contact; indirect contact with articles recently contaminated by infective nasopharyngeal secretions; annual influenza vaccine now includes protection against H1N1; abrupt onset of symptoms within 1–2 days of infection
Avian Influenza A/ H5N1 Virus (Avian flu, Bird flu)	Avian influenza A virus of the H5 and H7 subtypes; Avian Influenza able to cross the species barrier; of most concern is the H5N1 subtype distribution: evolving issue, refer to www.who.int or www.cdc.gov	Orthomyxoviridae – Influenza virus	high fever, influenza-like symptoms. diarrhea, vomiting, abdominal pain, chest pain, bleeding from nose and gums, respiratory distress, hoarseness, pneumonia; **Category C bioterrorism agent**	principle transmission: close contact with dead or sick birds; no efficient human-to-human transmission; incubation: 2–8 days but up to 17 days; evolving issue, refer to www.who.int or www.cdc.gov

Japanese encephalitis virus (JE)	RNA genome; reservoir: pigs and birds; associated with rice paddies and pig farms; widespread in Asia and occurs in New Guinea and Australia	acute encephalitis can progress to paralysis, seizures, coma and death; majority of infections are subclinical; aggressive encephalitis may have a prodrome of 2–4 days	mosquito bite of *Culex tritaeniorhynchus*, *annulirostris* and *vishnu* groups; incubation: 4–21 days; inactivated JE vaccine is available
JC virus (JCV)	DNA genome; reservoir: humans; worldwide distribution	primary infection does not exhibit clinical illness; progressive multifocal leukoencephalopathy; rapidly progressive focal neurologic deficits, hemiparesis, visual field deficits, cognitive impairment, aphasia, ataxia, cranial nerve deficits; later cortical blindness, quadriparesis, profound dementia and coma; rapid deterioration and death within 6 months	little is known about transmission or events during primary infection probably requires sustained close contact; no definitive evidence of perinatal transmission with maternal viruria
Junin virus (Argentinian hemorrhagic fever)	RNA genome; reservoir: rodents; limited agricultural areas in Argentina	slow onset with fever, malaise, headache and muscular pains; petechiae on the upper body and bleeding from the nose and gums; disease progresses to the hemorrhagic phase; **Category A bioterrorism agent**	carried by the local rodent Calomys laucha and C. musculinus; sharp seasonal pattern of occurrence between February and August; seen in farm hands who inhale virus secreted in urine or droppings as the soil is disturbed; incubation: 7–14 days
Kyasanur Forest disease virus (KFD)	RNA genome; reservoir: infected monkeys; limited to Karnataka State, India	symptoms of KFD begin suddenly with fever, headache, severe muscle pain, cough, dehydration, gastrointestinal symptoms and bleeding; abnormally low blood pressure, low platelet, red blood cell, and white blood cell counts. After 1–2 weeks of symptoms, illness is biphasic and second wave of symptoms experienced at the beginning of the third week: fever and signs of encephalitis; **Category C bioterrorism agent**	tick bite or by contact with an infected animal, such as sick or recently dead monkey, shrew, bat; incubation period: 3–8 days

(continued)

Name + (AKA)	Description	Family/Genus	Infections and Syndromes	Transmission and Incubation
LaCrosse virus (LAC)	RNA genome; reservoir: unknown	Bunyaviridae – Bunyavirus	usually asymptomatic or mild illness with headache; rare cause of aseptic meningitis, encephalitis, flaccid paralysis	infected mosquito bite; incubation: usually 5–15 days
Lassa virus (Lassa fever)	RNA genome; reservoir: rodents; geographic distribution: West Africa, rare cases in Europe, Japan and United States	Arenaviridae – Arenavirus	initially sore throat; low back pain; conjunctivitis; fever, headache, myalgia, cough, vomiting, retrosternal pain, lymphopenia, thrombocytopenia, mucosal hemorrhage, multisystem failure; **Category A bioterrorism agent**	ingestion of contaminated food or infected rodents; direct contact with infected rodent droppings; inhalation of aerosolized urine and drippings; incubation: 6–21 days
Klassevirus	RNA genome; reservoir: humans; newly identified in 2009	Picornaviridae – Picornavirus	diarrhea, gastrointeritis	stool and sewerage; incubation: unknown
Machupo virus (Bolivian hemorrhagic fever, BHF)	RNA genome; reservoir: rodents; occurs sporadically and/or epidemics in small villages of rural northeast Bolivia	Arenaviridae – Arenavirus	fever, headache, myalgia, cough, vomiting, retrosternal pain, lymphopenia, thrombocytopenia, mucosal hemorrhage, multisystem failure; chronic: deafness, spontaneous abortion, loss of coordination, hair loss **Category A bioterrorism agent**	ingestion of contaminated food or infected rodents; direct contact with infected rodent droppings; inhalation of aerosolized urine and droppings; incubation: 7–14 days
Marburg virus (Marburg hemorrhagic fever)	RNA genome; reservoir: unknown (monkeys and African fruit bats are susceptible, incidental hosts)	Filoviridae – Filovirus	acute infection: sudden onset high fever, malaise, myalgias, vomiting, diarrhea, maculopapular rash, renal/hepatic involvement, hemorrhagic diathesis, involvement of liver, pancreas, kidney, CNS, and heart; leukopenia, thrombocytopenia; **Category A bioterrorism agent**	direct contact with infected blood, secretions, organs, or semen; aerosol; contaminated syringes and needles; incubation: 2–21 days
Molluscum contagiosum virus (MCV)	DNA genome; reservoir: humans; worldwide distribution	Poxviridae/ Chordopoxvirinae – Molluscipoxvirus	children/teenagers: molluscum contagiosum lesions appear on face, trunk and limbs with ocular involvement; teenagers and adults: lower abdomen, pubis area, inner thighs and genitalia; small firm umbilicate papule with smooth, waxy surface; 10–20 lesions may be present for months; spontaneously resolves (avg. 2 months, as long as 2 years)	skin to skin in children; sexual transmission in adults; including autoinoculation; contact with fomites; incubation: 1 week to several months

Monkeypox virus	DNA genome; reservoir: humans, rodents; distribution: West Africa	Poxviridae/ Chordopoxvirinae – Orthopoxvirus	similar to, but much less serious than smallpox except for greater tendency to produce both lymphadenopathy and skin lesions that occur in "crops"	person to person; smallpox vaccination protective
Mumps virus (infectious parotitis)	RNA genome; reservoir: humans; worldwide distribution	Paramyxovirida – Rubulavirus	presents with mild symptoms, slight fever; enlarged parotid glands; mumps, complications: orchitis; oophoritis; polyarthritis; pancreatitis; meningoencephalitis	airborne; droplet; direct contact with saliva of infected person; incubation: 16–18 days; vaccine-preventable (MMR)
Murray Valley encephalitis virus (Australian "X" disease)	RNA genome; reservoir: birds, rabbits, kangaroos; present in Australia, Papua-New Guinea	Flaviviridae – Flavivirus	usually asymptomatic or mild illness with headache; rare cause of aseptic meningitis, encephalitis, flaccid paralysis	mosquito (C. annulisostris) bite; incubation: 5–15 days
Newcastle virus (Newcastle disease virus, NDV)	RNA genome; reservoir: birds; worldwide distribution	Paramyxoviridae – Rubulavirus	conjunctivitis	direct contact with secretions, feces
Nipah virus (Nipah virus encephalitis)	RNA genome; reservoir: fruit bats; found in Malaysia	Paramyxovirida – Paramyxovirus	fever, headache; myalgia; sore throat; thrombocytopenia; encephalitis; seizures; coma; **Category C bioterrorism agent**	close contact with infected pigs; incubation: 4–18 days
Norovirus (Norwalk-like viruses, NLV)	RNA genome; reservoir: humans; worldwide distribution	Caliciviridae – Norovirus	gastroenteritis acute onset: vomiting, watery non-bloody diarrhea, abdominal cramps, myalgia, malaise, headache, dehydration); outbreaks in close quarters settings; food outbreaks in nursing homes and cruise ships	fecal-oral; direct person to person contact, contact fecally contaminated food or water; droplets from vomitus; incubation: 12–48 hours, symptoms last 24–60 hours
Norwalk virus (Norwalk agent, epidemic viral gastroenteritis, acute infectious nonbacterial gastroenteritis, epidemic diarrhea/vomiting, winter vomiting disease)	RNA genome; reservoir: humans; worldwide distribution	Caliciviridae – Calicivirus	acute infection: self-limited; mild to moderate disease with clinical symptoms of nausea, vomiting, diarrhea, abdominal pain, myalgia, headache, malaise, low grade fever; GI symptoms generally last 24-48 hours	fecal-oral; contact; airborne transmission from fomite suggested to explain outbreaks; ingestion of raw shellfish and contaminated vegetables; incubation: 10–50 hours, usually 24–48 hours

(continued)

Name + (AKA)	Description	Family/Genus	Infections and Syndromes	Transmission and Incubation
Omsk hemorrhagic fever virus	RNA genome; reservoir: muskrats; western Siberia regions	Flaviviridae	sudden onset of fever, headache, severe muscle pain, cough dehydration, gastrointestinal symptoms and bleeding; abnormally low blood pressure, low platelet, red blood cell and white blood cell counts; illness biphasic second wave of symptoms at beginning of third week: fever, encephalitis; **Category C bioterrorism agent**	tick bite or by contact with an infected muskrat; milk of infected goats or sheep; incubation period: 3–8 days
Orf virus (Orf, ecthyma contagiosum, scabby mouth, sore mouth, contagious pustular dermatosis, infectious pustular dermatitis)	DNA genome; reservoir: humans, sheep, goats	Poxviridae/ Chordopoxvirinae – Parapoxvirus	presents 1 to 4 papules on hands progresses through 6 stages, each lasts approx. 6 days; typically leaves no scar; lesions are painless and persist for approx. 6 weeks; autoinoculation of the eye may lead to serious sequelae	contact with skinning of deer, reindeer, chamois, Japanese serow; infected lesions on animals or from fomites (e.g. fences, barn doors, feeding troughs, and shears); incubation: 3–6 days
Parainfluenza virus (Type 1 known as Sendai virus)	RNA genomes; serotypes 1–4; reservoir: humans, pigs, mice, other animals; worldwide distribution	Paramyxovirida – Paramyxovirus	croup, common cold syndrome, laryngotracheobronchitis, bronchiolitis, pneumonia	droplet; incubation: 1–4 days
Poliovirus (infantile paralysis, Heine-Medin disease)	RNA genomes; serotypes 1–3; reservoir: humans	Picornaviridae – Enterovirus	poliomyelitis, aseptic meningitis, encephalitis, paralytic syndrome, post poliomyelitis syndrome, vaccine associated paralytic poliomyelitis	fecal-oral (direct); saliva, feces, contaminated sewage and water (indirect); incubation: 9–10 days (range 5–35 days); vaccine preventable
Powassan virus	RNA genome; reservoir: rodents and wild mammals; distribution: Russia, USA, Canada	Flaviviridae – Flavivirus	encephalitis with fever and nonspecific neurologic sequelae	infected deer tick bite; incubation 7–14 days
Pseudocowpox virus (bovine papular stomatitis, milker's virus nodules, paravaccinia)	DNA genome; reservoir: humans and cattle	Poxviridae/ Chordopoxvirinae – Parapoxvirus	symptoms similar to Orf	infected lesions on teats of cattle

Virus	Family – Genus	Genome/reservoir/distribution	Disease/symptoms	Transmission/incubation
Rabies virus (rabies)	Rhabdoviridae – Lyssavirus	RNA genome; reservoir: animals; worldwide distribution	virus replicates at site of bite and then infects central nervous system; fever, excitation, dilated pupils, excessive lacrimation, salivation, hydrophobia due to spasms of throat muscles, eventually death	bite or wound infected with saliva from rabid animal; incubation: 3–8 weeks; vaccine is available for both animals and humans
Respiratory syncytial virus (RSV)	Paramyxovirida – Pneumovirus	RNA genome; reservoir: humans; worldwide distribution	bronchiolitis in infants and young children; pneumonia and tracheobronchitis; crowding, schools and daycare centers, increase attack rate	droplet; direct contact with infectious secretions and fomites; incubation: 2–8 days (median 4.4 days)
Rhinovirus	Picornaviridae – Enterovirus	small RNA genomes; more than 120 serotypes; reservoir: humans; seasonal worldwide distribution	common cold, laryngitis, tracheitis and bronchitis; may have role in acute sinus infections; otitis media, asthma, and chronic bronchitis	direct close contact; airborne droplets; fomites; self-inoculation (finger to nose, finger to eye); incubation: 1–4 days
Rift Valley Fever virus	Bunyaviridae – Phlebovirus	RNA genome; reservoir: unknown	fever, encephalitis, hemorrhagic fever, blindness, hemorrhagic hepatitis	mosquito bite; direct exposure to infected animals; incubation: usually 2–14 days
Rotavirus (gastroenteritis)	Reoviridae – Rotavirus	RNA genome; reservoir: humans, zoonotic; worldwide distribution	occurs mostly in infants and young children; vomiting, followed by severe diarrhea lasts 4–5 days	fecal–oral; possible airborne; may be present in contaminated water; incubation: 24–72 hours
Rubella virus (German measles, 3-day measles)	Togaviridae – Rubivirus	RNA genome; reservoir: humans; worldwide distribution	mild febrile infectious disease with diffuse macular rash; congenital rubella syndrome	contact with nasopharyngeal secretions of infected person; droplet; congenital; incubation: 14–17 days (range 14–21 days); vaccine preventable
Rubeola virus (red measles)	Paramyxoviridae – Morbillivirus	RNA genome; reservoir: humans; worldwide distribution	coryza, conjunctivitis, red maculopapular rash, Koplik spots; complications: bronchopneumonia	airborne; droplets; contaminated fomites; incubation: 7–10 days; vaccine preventable (MMR)

(continued)

Name + (AKA)	Description	Family/Genus	Infections and Syndromes	Transmission and Incubation
Severe Febrile Thrombocytopenia Syndrome virus (SFTSV)	RNA genome; reservoir: ticks; newly identified virus in 2009 in China.	Bunyaviridae – Bunyavirus	fever, fatigue, conjunctival congestion, thrombocytopenia, leukocytopenia, multiorgan dysfunction; diarrhea, abdominal pain; proteinuria; hematuria; high fatality	Tick-borne; Human to human transmission through contaminated blood contact; incubation: unknown
Sindbis virus (Ockelbo virus, Pogosta virus, Karelian fever virus, Babanki virus)	RNA genome; reservoir: birds; found in Africa, India, Southeast Asia, Europe, Philippines, Australia, Russia	Togaviridae – Alphavirus	fever, arthritis, rash	mosquito bite; incubation: 3–21 days
St. Louis encephalitis virus (SLE)	RNA genome; reservoir: birds; present only in the Americas	Flaviviridae – Flavivirus	encephalitis; eighth cranial nerve is affected; may have hepatitis	mosquito bite: *Cx. nigripalpus* (Florida), *Cx. tarsalis* (western U.S.), *Cx. pipiens* (midwest); incubation: 4–21 days
Tick-borne encephalitis virus (three subtypes: European; Far Eastern; Siberian) (TBEV)	RNA genome; reservoir: ticks; endemic in temperate regions of Europe and Asia	Flavivirus	First phase: nonspecific febrile illness with headache, myalgia, and fatigue; usually lasts for several days; followed by an afebrile and relatively asymptomatic period; Second phase: central nervous system involvement resulting in aseptic meningitis, encephalitis, or myelitis; cranial nerve involvement, bulbar syndrome, and acute flaccid paralysis of the upper extremities; European subtype: associated with milder disease, a case-fatality ratio of <2%, and neurologic sequelae in 30% of patients; Far Eastern subtype: associated with a more severe disease course, including a case-fatality ratio of 20%–40% and higher rates of severe neurologic sequelae; Siberian subtype: associated with chronic or progressive disease and has a case-fatality ratio of 2%–3%; **Category C bioterrorism agent**	bite of an infected tick of the *Ixodes* species; ingesting unpasteurized dairy products (such as milk and cheese) from infected goats, sheep, or cows; approximately two-thirds of infections are asymptomatic; incubation: 4–28 days (milk-borne exposure is usually shorter: 3–4 days)

Varicella-zoster virus (human herpesvirus 3, varicella virus [Chickenpox], herpes zoster, shingles, (VZV)	DNA genome; reservoir: humans; worldwide distribution	Herpesviridae/ Alphaherpesvirinae – Varicellovirus	chickenpox (varicella); shingles (dermatomal zoster, zoster); disseminated infection, perinatal varicella, cerebellar ataxia, encephalitis, cerebral angiitis after herpes zoster ophthalmicus, meningitis, transverse myelitis, varicella pneumonitis, myositis, myocarditis, nephritis, hepatitis; associated with Guillain-Barre syndrome, Reye's syndrome	perinatal; person to person by direct contact; droplet or airborne spread of vesicle fluids or respiratory secretions of chickenpox patients; direct contact of vesicle fluids of zoster patients; indirect contact with articles soiled with discharges from vesicles and mucous membranes of persons with chickenpox; incubation: 2-3 weeks (usually 14-16 days); chickenpox, vaccine preventable; shingles, vaccine preventable
Variola virus (smallpox)	DNA genome; reservoir: humans; global eradication, 1979	Poxviridae/ Chordopoxvirinae – Orthopoxvirus	fever, malaise, backache, exanthem appears within 2-4 days and evolves macules to pustules to crusts, lesions begin on face and extremities; scarring may be severe; mortality: 30-50%; **Category A bioterrorism agent**	person to person by direct contact; droplet or airborne spread of vesicle fluids or respiratory secretions; indirect contact with articles soiled with discharges from vesicles and mucous membranes of persons with smallpox; incubation: 7–19 days with prodrome 2–4 days; limited vaccine available from CDC
Venezuelan equine encephalitis virus (VEE, Everglades virus, Mucambo virus, Tonate virus)	RNA genome; reservoir: rodents; found in the Americas	Togaviridae – Alphavirus	fever, severe headache, back pain, myalgias, prostration, chills, nausea, vomiting, and weakness; may progress from encephalitis to death; encephalomyelitis; **Category B bioterrorism agent**	mosquito bite; incubation: 2–6 days

(continued)

Name + (AKA)	Description	Family/Genus	Infections and Syndromes	Transmission and Incubation
Vesiculovirus (vesicular stomatitis diseases)	RNA genome; reservoir: sand fly	Rhabdoviridae – Vesiculovirus	high fever, malaise, retrobulbar pain on motion of eyes; oral mucosal vesicular lesions; meningeoencephalitis	bite of infected sand fly; incubation: up to 6 days, usually 3–4 days
West Nile virus	RNA genome; reservoir: birds; worldwide distribution	Flaviviridae – Flavivirus	fever, arthralgia, rash, encephalitis; in <15%, acute aseptic meningitis or encephalitis; flaccid paralysis, hepatitis, pancreatis, myocarditis, chorioretinitis; elderly at greatest risk of severe disease	*Culex* mosquito bite; incubation: 3–12 days
Western equine encephalitis virus (WEE)	RNA genome; reservoir: birds; found in the Americas	Togaviridae – Alphavirus	fever, severe headache, back pain, myalgias, prostration, chills, nausea, vomiting, and weakness; may progress from encephalitis to death; encephalomyelitis; **Category B bioterrorism agent**	mosquito bite; incubation: 5–15 days
Yellow fever virus (YF)	RNA genome; reservoir: humans, monkeys; found in tropical America (south of Panama Canal), sub-Saharan/tropical Africa	Flaviviridae – Flavivirus	sudden onset of fever, slow pulse, headache; severe cases: intense albuminuria, jaundice, hemorrhage, hematemesis; hemorrhagic fever, hepatitis, nephritis, often fatal; **Category C bioterrorism agent**	mosquito (*Aedes* sps.) bite; incubation: 2–5 days; immunization available and required by many countries
Prions				
Creutzfeldt-Jakob disease (CJD, spongiform encephalopathies)	Proteinaceous infectious particles, no DNA or RNA present; reservoir: infected human tissue	prion; "unconventional slow virus"	prion diseases cause neurological symptoms: confusion, loss of muscle control, tremors, loss of coordination and dementia with rapid progression to death after the symptoms appear; prions are much more resistant to normal sterilization and require special care in handling and sterilizing instruments used on affected patients; 4 types of Creutzfeldt-Jakob disease (CJD): sporadic, iatrogenic, familial, and new variant seen in younger people	contact with infected tissue, such as transplants, CSF or brain matter, through contaminated medical devices, and potentially through ingestion of infected tissue; long incubation period of 10–30 years, depending on type

C-J variant (mad cow disease, bovine spongiform encephalopathy)	proteinaceous infectious particles, no DNA or RNA present; reservoir: infected human tissue	prion; "unconventional slow virus"	prion diseases cause neurological symptoms: confusion, loss of muscle control, tremors, loss of coordination, and dementia with rapid progression to death after the symptoms appear; prions are much more resistant to normal sterilization and require special care in handling and sterilizing instruments used on affected patients	contact with infected tissue, such as transplants, CSF, or brain matter, through contaminated medical devices, and potentially through ingestion of infected tissue; long incubation period of 10–30 years, depending on type
Fatal familial insomnia (FFI)	proteinaceous infectious particles, no DNA or RNA present; reservoir: infected human tissue	prion; "unconventional slow virus"	prion diseases cause neurological symptoms: confusion, loss of muscle control, tremors, loss of coordination, and dementia with rapid progression to death after the symptoms appear; prions are much more resistant to normal sterilization and require special care in handling and sterilizing instruments used on affected patients	contact with infected tissue, such as transplants, CSF, brain matter, through contaminated medical devices, and potentially through ingestion of infected tissue; long incubation period of 10–30 years, depending on type
Gerstmann-Straussler-Scheinker syndrome (GSS)	proteinaceous infectious particles, no DNA or RNA present; reservoir: infected human tissue	prion; "unconventional slow virus"	prion diseases cause neurological symptoms: confusion, loss of muscle control, tremors, loss of coordination, and dementia with rapid progression to death after the symptoms appear; prions are much more resistant to normal sterilization and require special care in handling and sterilizing instruments used on affected patients	contact with infected tissue, such as transplants, CSF, brain matter, through contaminated medical devices, and potentially through ingestion of infected tissue; long incubation period of 10–30 years, depending on type
Kuru	proteinaceous infectious particles, no DNA or RNA present; reservoir: infected human tissue	prion; "unconventional slow virus"	prion diseases cause neurological symptoms: confusion, loss of muscle control, tremors, loss of coordination, and dementia with rapid progression to death after the symptoms appear; prions are much more resistant to normal sterilization and require special care in handling and sterilizing instruments used on affected patients	related to cannibalism, through infected tissue; transmitted to women and children during rituals associated with preparing body for final disposition

References

Brooks GF, Butel JS, Morse SA. *Jawetz, Melnick, & Adelberg's Medical Microbiology.* 24th ed. New York: Appleton-Lange Medical Books/McGraw-Hill; 2010.

Forbes B, Sahm DF, Weissfeld AS. *Bailey & Scott's Diagnostic Microbiology.* 12th ed. St. Louis: Mosby-Yearbook/Harcourt Health Sciences; 2007.

Gilbert DN, Moellering RC, Eliopoulos GM, Chambers HF, Saag MS. *The Sanford Guide to Antimicrobial Therapy 2011.* 41st ed. Sperryville, VA: Antimicrobial Therapy, Inc.; 2011.

Grota P, ed. *APIC Text of Infection Control and Epidemiology,* 4th ed. Washington, DC: Association for Professionals in Infection Control and Epidemiology, 2014.

Greninger AL, Holtz L, Kang G, Ganem D, Wang D, DeRisi JL. Serological Evidence of Human klassevirus Infection. *Clin Vaccine Immunol* 2010; 17(10):1584-1588.

Heymann DL, ed. *Control of Communicable Diseases Manual,* 19th ed. Baltimore: American Public Health Association, United Book Press, Inc.; 2008.

Mahon CR, Lehman, DC, Manuselis G, eds. *Textbook of Diagnostic Microbiology,* 4th ed. St. Louis: W.B. Saunders Company/Harcourt Health Sciences; 2010.

Mandell GL, Bennett JE, Dolin R, eds. *Principles and Practice of Infectious Diseases,* 7th ed. St. Louis: Churchill Livingstone/Harcourt Health Sciences; 2010.

Pickering LK, ed. *2009 Red Book, Report of the Committee on Infectious Diseases,* 28th ed. Elk Grove: American Academy of Pediatrics; 2009.

Porter, RS and Kaplan, JL, eds. *The Merck Manual of Diagnosis and Therapy,* 19th ed. Whitehouse Station: Merck & Company; 2011.

Tortora GJ, Funke BR, Case CL. *Microbiology, An Introduction,* 10th ed. San Francisco: Benjamin Cummings Publishing; 2009.

Versalovic J, Carroll KC, Jorgensen JH, Funke G, Landry ML, Warnock DW, eds. *Manual of Clinical Microbiology,* 12th ed. Washington, DC: American Society of Microbiology Press; 2011.

Yu XJ, Liang MF, Zhang SY, Liu Y, Li JD, Sun YL, et al. Fever with Thrombocytopenia Associated with a Novel Bunyavirus in China. *N Engl J Med* 2011; 364:1523-1532.

Additional Resources

APIC Text Online. 2011. http://text.apic.org/

American Society for Microbiology. http://www.asm.org

Arenavirus. In: CDC Special Pathogens Branch. Available at http://www.cdc .gov/ncidod/dvrd/spb/mnpages/dispages/arena.htm. Accessed 2/2/2012.

Centers for Disease Control and Prevention. http://www.cdc.gov

CDC Seasonal Influenza (Flu). In: Key Facts about Human Infections with Variant Viruses. Available at http://www.cdc.gov/flu/swineflu/keyfacts-variant.htm. Accessed 3/9/2012.

Charrel RN, Fagbo S, Moureau G, Alqahtani MH, Temmam S, Lamballerie XD. Alkhurma Hemorrhagic Fever Virus in *Ornithodoros savignyi* Ticks. In: EID. Available at http://wwwnc.cdc.gov/eid/article/13/1/06-1094_article. htm. Accessed 2/16/2012.

Crimean-Congo Hemorrhagic Fever. In: CDC Special Pathogens Branch. Available at http://www.cdc.gov/ncidod/dvrd/spb/mnpages/dispages/cchf. htm. Accessed 2/17/2012.

Crisis and Emergency Risk Communication Course (CERC). In: Pandemic Influenza Overview & Objectives. Available at http://emergency.cdc.gov/ cerc/panflu/overview.asp. Accessed 2/16/2012.

Disease Information for Tick-borne hemorrhagic fevers. In: DiagnosisPro. Available at http://en.diagnosispro.com/disease_information-for/tick-borne-hemorrhagic-fevers/20416. Accessed 2/17/2012.

Emerging & Re-emerging Infectious Diseases. In: NIH Education, Understanding Infectious Diseases. Available at http://science.education.nih.gov/ supplements/nih1/diseases/guide/understanding1.htm Accessed 1/4/2012.

Haemorrhagic fevers, Viral. In: Health Topics, World Health Organization (WHO). Available at http://www.who.int/topics/haemorrhagic_fevers_viral/en/index.html. Accessed 2/16/2012.

Health-care Associated Infections. http://www.cdc.gov/hai/

Influenza Type A Viruses and Subtypes. In: CDC Seasonal Influenza (Flu). Available at http://www.cdc.gov/flu/avianflu/influenza-a-virus-subtypes.htm. Accessed 2/16/2012.

Information on H3N2 Variant Influenza A Viruses. In: CDC Seasonal Influenza (Flu). Available at http://www.cdc.gov/flu/swineflu/influenza-variant-viruses-h3n2v.htm. Accessed 3/9/2012.

Kyasanur Forest Disease. In: CDC Special Pathogens Branch. Available at http://www.cdc.gov/ncidod/dvrd/spb/mnpages/dispages/kyasanur.htm. Accessed 2/17/2012.

Liu Y, Li Q, Hu W, Wu J, Wang Y, Mei L, Walker DH, Ren J, Yu XJ. Person-to-Person Transmission of Severe Fever with Thrombocytopenia Syndrome Virus. Vector Borne Zoonotic Dis. 2012 Feb;12(2):156-60. Available at http://www.ncbi.nlm.nih.gov/pubmed/21955213. Accessed 3/8/2012.

Micromedex Healthcare Series. www.micromedex.com/products/hcs/

Omsk Hemorrhagic Fever. In: CDC Special Pathogens Branch. Available at http://www.cdc.gov/ncidod/dvrd/spb/mnpages/dispages/omsk.htm. Accessed 2/17/2012.

SHEA Guidelines and Resources. Compendium of Strategies to Prevent HAIs. Available at http://www.shea-online.org/GuidelinesResources/CompendiumofStrategiestoPreventHAIs.aspx

The Big Picture Book of Viruses. http://www.virology.net/Big_Virology/BVDiseaseList.html

The Sanford Guide to Antimicrobial Therapy 41st edition, 2011. http://www.sanfordguide.com

Tick-borne Encephalitis. In: CDC Special Pathogens Branch. Available at http://www.cdc.gov/ncidod/dvrd/spb/mnpages/dispages/TBE.htm. Accessed 2/16/2012.

Viral Hemorrhagic Fevers. In: CDC Special Pathogens Branch. Available at http://www.cdc.gov/ncidod/dvrd/spb/mnpages/dispages/vhf.htm. Accessed 2/16/2012.

Viral Hemorrhagic Fever Information. In: Bioterrorism Information, John Hopkins Medicine. Available at http://www.hopkinsmedicine.org/heic/ bioterrorism/facts/vhf.html. Accessed 2/16/2012.

Yellow Fever. In: CDC – Yellow Fever. Available at http://www.cdc.gov/ yellowfever/. Accessed 2/16/2012.

Yellow fever. In: WHO Global Alert and Response (GAR). Available at http://www.who.int/csr/disease/yellowfev/en/index.html. http://www.who .int/topics/yellow_fever/en/index.html. Accessed 2/16/2012.

Yellow fever. In: WHO Media centre. Available at http://www.who.int/ mediacentre/factsheets/fs100/en/. Accessed 2/16/2012.

World Health Organization. http://www.who.int

Chapter Five

———

Common Commensals and Other Normal Flora

The human body contains approximately 10^{13} cells and harbors approximately 10^{14} bacteria. An estimated five hundred to one thousand different bacterial species reside on or in the body. These bacteria are considered normal flora and are defined as microbes that normally live in and on the body without causing infection and/or disease. Normal flora are divided into two types: resident flora, which are always present, and transient flora, which may be present for a few days, weeks, or months. Colonization occurs when resident flora grow and multiply without causing tissue invasion and infections. In certain situations, such as in the immunocompromised host, normal flora colonization can become pathogenic and result in infection. Transient flora are troublesome due to the ease of transmission if hand hygiene is not consistently practiced. Note: CDC and National Healthcare Safety Network (NHSN) surveillance definitions of healthcare associated infections refer to "skin contaminants" as "common commensals." For more information, please visit http://www.cdc.gov/NHSN.

Three relationships existing between the body (host) and normal flora are:

1. Commensal in which normal flora neither harm nor benefit the host (i.e., microbes on the skin)
2. Mutual in which both flora and host benefit (i.e., *E. coli*, normal GI flora, synthesizes vitamin K)
3. Pathogenic in which the microbes cause harm to the host (i.e., normal flora are disturbed and host defenses are decreased, resulting in microbes becoming opportunistic and invading tissue leading to infections and disease states)

The four major body sites contain normal flora unique to each site.

Skin

1. Moist areas of axilla, perineum, and toe webs promote dense bacterial colonization.

2. Drier areas comprising the bulk of the skin surfaces promote less dense bacterial colonization. Most common normal flora of skin (new CDC term is "**common commensals**") are *Staphylococcus epidermidis, Staphylococcus aureus, Corynebacteria,* and *Streptococci,* with Gram-negative bacteria more common in the moist areas.

Respiratory tract

1. Normal flora of the upper respiratory tract, including the nasopharyngeal area, are *Staphylococcus aureus* and *Staphylococcus epidermidis.* The nasopharynx may also harbor potential pathogens, such as *Streptococcus pneumoniae, Neisseria meningitidis,* and *Haemophilus influenzae.*
2. The bronchi and lower respiratory tract do not normally contain microbes. The presence of microbes is indicative of colonization or infection.

Gastrointestinal tract

1. The GI tract contains the bulk of normal flora with the large intestine containing 10^9 to 10^{11} bacteria per gram of feces.
2. Mouth: More than 200 bacterial species are present with the most common being *Streptococci, Lactobacilli,* and *Corynebacteria.*
3. Esophagus and stomach: Organisms are usually transient and remain sparse except for the most acid-tolerant. *Helicobacter pylorus* is a potential pathogen as noted by the formation of certain ulcers.
4. Small intestine: Normal flora consist of *Lactobacilli, Enterobacteriaceae, Streptococci* and *Bacteroides.*
5. Large intestine: Flora are dense and up to 1,000 species can be present. Anaerobes (*Bacteroides, Bifidobacterium, Streptococci,* and *Clostridia*) are the predominant flora.

Normal flora in the small and large intestines metabolize compounds and synthesize vitamins, but can also serve as opportunistic pathogens if the intestinal wall is compromised.

Genitourinary tract

1. The kidney, bladder, and ureters do not normally contain microbes.
2. Normal flora are found in the vagina, external genitalia and the distal urethra. The vagina is colonized with *Lactobacilli, Corynebacteria, Staphylococci, Streptococci* and *E. coli.* Transient microbes such as *Candida* spp. can be pathogenic if the protective nature of vaginal normal flora is compromised. The distal urethra and external genitalia contain microbes that are common skin and large intestine flora, including *Staphylococcus epidermidis, Staphylococcus aureus, Enterococcus faecalis, E. coli, Proteus* spp., *Corynebacteria and Streptococci.*

The functions of normal flora in and on the body are complex and crucial. Beneficial functions by normal flora to the host include:

1. Synthesizing and excreting vitamins
2. Preventing pathogen colonization and opportunistic infections by constant stimulation of the host's immune system
3. Producing substances that inhibit or kill microbes that are not a part of normal flora

Table

The following table presents basic concepts for an understanding of normal flora per body site. Note that the table:

- Lists the normal flora by body site
- Provides comments regarding specimen collection considerations

The reader is encouraged to refer to the Bacteria Chapter for information regarding genus, description, infections and mode of transmission.

Body Site	Normal Flora	Special Considerations of Specimen Collection
Blood	None	Disinfect venipuncture site with approved skin antiseptic, such as iodine compounds (i.e. tincture of iodine or betadine) or Chlorhexidine to prevent introducing contaminants into blood culture media; Draw when patient febrile prior to treatment; Draw 2 sets from separate sites; If patient has IV line, only as last resort, draw blood below line to prevent dilution from IV solution; ideally another site should be sought for specimen collection; Adults: Draw 10–20 mL increases chance of isolating organism; Infants and small children: Draw 1–5 mL, less than 1 mL may not be adequate to detect pathogens; If patient has a central line, draw one set of blood cultures from the line and the second by venipuncture.
		Probable contaminant: *Bacillus* spp, *Corynebacterium* spp, *Propionibacterium acnes, Micrococcus, viridans* group *Streptococci* or coagulase-negative *Staphylococci* in one of several cultures; Multiple microbes in one of several cultures; Microbe causing infection at primary site is not the same as microbe in blood culture.
		Probable pathogen: Same microbe in repeated cultures from different sites or different times; *Enterococci* blood culture in patient with endocarditis; Gram-negative rods in blood culture in patient with clinical Gram-negative sepsis; *Enterobacteriaceae, Streptococcus pneumoniae, Streptococcus pyogenes,* and Gram-negative anaerobes in blood culture; Normal flora in blood cultures from immunosuppressed or patients with prosthetic devices

(continued)

Body Site	Normal Flora	Special Considerations of Specimen Collection
Ears		
External	Few *Staphylococcus epidermidis, Lactobacilli, Pneumococci, Propionibacterium acnes, Staphylococcus aureus*	Moisten swab with sterile saline to remove crusts, Discard and use sterile swab, Firmly rotate in external canal to obtain specimen
Middle and Inner	None	Clean ear canal with mild soap solution; Aspirate fluid; If eardrum ruptured, collect fluid in flexible shaft swab
Eyes (cornea)	Few *Staphylococcus epidermidis, Lactobacillus* spp.	Use separate swabs premoistened with sterile saline to sample both eyes (uninfected eye serves as control); If specimen not grossly purulent, large inoculum and various media may be used, including conjunctival scrapings
GI Tract		
Stomach	Microbes are transient due to high acidity levels	In infants, stomach aspirate may be collected for AFB smears. See Respiratory section.
Small intestine	*Bacteroides, E. coli, Lactobacilli, Streptococci*	
Large intestine	*Actinomyces, Bacteroides* spp., *Bifidobacterium, Citrobacter* spp., *Clostridium perfringens,* other *Clostridia, Eikenella corrodens, Enterobacter* spp.; *Enterococcus, E. coli, Eubacterium, Fusobacterium, Klebsiella* spp., *Lactobacillus* spp., *Morganella* spp., *Peptostreptococcus, Porphyromonas, Prevotella, Providencia* spp., *Proteus* spp., *Serratia* spp., *Streptococcus* spp., *Veillonella* (**More than 400 species with 95–99% being *Bacteroides, Bifidobacterium, Clostridium,* and *Peptostreptococcus*)**	Stool for routine culture - Instruct patient not to retrieve from toilet; Volume of liquid stool at least equal to 5 mL or if from formed stool must be pea-sized specimen; Stool for viral culture must be refrigerated if not placed on media within 2 hours of collection; Rectal swabs used to identify *Campylobacter* spp., *Shigella* spp., *Neisseria gonorrhoeae, Streptococcus pyogenes,* VRE; Insert swab approximately 2.5 cm past anal sphincter; Stool for ova and parasites -Wait 7–10 days if patient has received antiparasitic compounds, barium, iron, metronidazole, tetracycline, Kaopectate, Milk of Magnesia, or Pepto-Bismol. Diapers - Using aseptic technique with a sterile tongue depressor, obtain the stool specimen from the diaper or line diaper with plastic wrap prior to specimen collection; Specimen may be obtained via rectal swab per hospital protocol.
GU Tract		
Bladder	None	
Kidneys	None	
Ureters	None	

(continued)

Body Site	Normal Flora	Special Considerations of Specimen Collection
Urine	None	Prevention of contamination by normal flora of vagina, perineum, anterior urethra most important consideration for clinically relevant specimen. Midstream - Female: Clean area with soap and water; Rinse with water; Hold labia apart and begin voiding in commode; After several mL have passed, collect midstream. Male: Clean glans with soap and water; Rinse with water; Retract foreskin; After several mL have passed, collect midstream.
		Urine from Foley catheter - Disinfect catheter collection port with 70% alcohol; Aspirate 5 – 10 mL of urine with syringe; Do not collect from Foley bag. Urine from straight (in and out) catheter - Insert catheter into bladder; Discard first 15 mL of urine; Collect remainder.
		Diapers - A urine bag may be applied, using aseptic technique, and monitored until at least 5ml are obtained for analysis. Suprapubic aspirate - Disinfect skin with appropriate antiseptic; Urine is withdrawn through percutaneously inserted needle; Note: Needle inserted above symphysis pubis through abdominal wall into full bladder.
Urethra (distal)	*Corynebacterium, Enterococci, Staphylococci, Streptococci, Lactobacillus*	Remove exudate from urethral orifice; Insert swab 2–4 cm into urethral lumen; Rotate swab 360 degrees for 2 seconds
External genitalia	*Bacteroides, Corynebacterium, Enterococcus faecalis, E. coli; Kingella, Peptostreptococcus, Prevotella, Proteus* spp., *Staphylococcus aureus, Staphylococcus epidermidis, Streptococcus viridans*	Genital lesions - Clean with sterile saline; Remove surface with sterile scalpel blade; Press swab against base of lesion
Uterus	None	Cervix - Remove mucus; Do not use lubricant on speculum; Swab deeply into endocervical canal
Vagina	*Corynebacterium, Enterococci, E. coli, Eubacterium, Gardnerella, Kingella, Lactobacillus, Mycoplasma, Peptococcus, Peptostreptococcus, Prevotella, Propionibacterium, Staphylococcus aureus, Staphylococcus epidermidis, Streptococcus viridans* and *saprophyticus, Veillonella*	Remove exudate and excessive secretions; Obtain specimen from mucosal membrane of vaginal vault with sterile swab. Bartholin cyst - Disinfect skin; Aspirate fluid with needle and syringe.

(continued)

Body Site	Normal Flora	Special Considerations of Specimen Collection
Respiratory Tract		
Bronchi	None	Procedures recommended to prevent contamination from upper respiratory flora are: • Bronchioalveolar lavage (BAL) - performed via bronchoscopy in which a specified amount of saline is infused into lung segment to obtain cells and protein of the pulmonary interstitial and alveolar spaces; Quantitative testing is performed. • Bronchial washing - performed via bronchoscopy with unspecified amount of saline in order to flush out tenacious secretions for testing. • Bronchial brush - performed via bronchoscopy using a protected catheter bronchial brush to obtain specimen; Colony counts greater than or equal to 1,000 organisms per mL considered an infection.
Nasopharynx	*Actinomyces, Bifidobacterium, Corynebacterium, Eubacterium, Fusobacterium, Lactobacillus, Moraxella, Peptostreptococcus, Porphyomonas, Prevotella, Propionibacterium, Staphylococcus aureus, Staphylococcus epidermidis, Streptococci, Veillonella*	Moisten swab with holding medium; Insert flexible NP swab through nose; Rotate moistened swab for 5 seconds in posterior nasopharynx; Throat - Swab posterior pharynx and tonsils
Upper	*Actinomyces, Bifidobacterium, Cardiobacterium, Eubacterium, Fusobacterium, Haemophilus* spp., *Gemella, Kingella, Klebsiella, Lactobacillus, Moraxella, Neisseria* spp., *Peptostreptococcus, Porphyromonas, Prevotella, Propionibacterium, Streptococcus pyogenes, Veillonella*	Sputum specimen among least clinically relevant but one of most frequent and time-consuming specimens. Instruct patient to rinse mouth with water and cough deeply; Consider distilled water in areas with high levels of microbes. Induced sputa from pediatric or uncooperative patients may be watery from saline nebulization. Gastric aspirates - Collected in the early AM prior to patient eating or getting out of bed; Gastric aspirates are for acid-fast bacilli (AFB) and collected from infants, young children, patients unable to produce sputum (Assumption: AFBs from respiratory tract are swallowed during night and will be present in stomach).
Lower	None	See Bronchi above

(continued)

Body Site	Normal Flora	Special Considerations of Specimen Collection
Oral (Mouth)	*Actinobacillus, Actinomyces, Bifidobacterium, Cardiobacterium, Eikenella corrodens, Eubacterium, Fusobacterium, Gemella, Haemophilus, Kingella, Lactobacilli, Micrococcus, Mycoplasma, Porphyromonas, Prevotella, Propionibacterium, Stomatococcus, Streptococcus viridans* group, *Veillonella* **(More than 200 species of bacteria found in oral cavity)**	Clean oral surface to remove plaque, saliva, and debris; Use periodontal scaler to obtain subgingival material
Sinuses	None	Aspiration of specimen performed by provider in the clinic or hospital setting using aseptic technique
Skin (including nails and hair)	Coagulase-negative *Staphylococcus* (CNS), *Corynebacterium, Micrococcus, Peptostreptococcus, Propionibacterium, Staphylococcus aureus, Staphylococcus epidermidis, Staphylococcus saprophyticus, Streptococcus pyogenes*	For skin bacterial cultures: Wipe with sterile water or sterile normal saline prior to specimen collection. For fungal cultures: Skin, hair or nail scrapings - Wipe nails or skin with 70% alcohol; Hair: Collect intact shaft; Nails: Send clippings of affected area; Skin: Scrape skin at leading edge of lesion
Spinal Fluid	None	Disinfect site with appropriate skin antiseptic prior to aspirating specimen; Consider volume needed for all testing requested; Never refrigerate cerebrospinal fluid for bacterial cultures; Immediate delivery to lab; Cannot delay from collection to testing; Antibiotic cannot be started until after collection

Invasive procedure specimens

Body Site	Normal Flora	Special Considerations of Specimen Collection
Body fluids (amniotic, abdominal, bile, synovial, pericardial, pleural)	None	Disinfect skin; Specimen collected via needle aspiration; 1 to 5 mL is adequate but larger volume of 5 to 10 mL is better
Bone	None	Specimen collected via bone biopsy usually performed in surgery or at the bedside using sterile technique

(continued)

Body Site	Normal Flora	Special Considerations of Specimen Collection
Catheter tips	None	Clean area around catheter with 70% alcohol; Remove catheter using aseptic technique and clip 5 cm of distal tip; Place in a sterile tube or cup and transport to lab immediately. Quantitative cultures obtained by rolling segment (tip of catheter) 4 times across agar with sterile forceps; Greater than or equal to 15 colonies clinically significant. Do not culture Foley catheters.
Tissue	None	Submit specimen to lab within 15 minutes to prevent drying; Small samples may add few drops of sterile saline to prevent drying
Wounds		
Abscess (lesion, pustule, ulcer, surgical wound)	None	Superficial: Wipe area with saline or sterile water; Swab along leading edge of wound. Deep: Wipe area with saline or sterile water; Aspirate material from wall or excise tissue sample.
Burns	None	Biopsy specimen preferred; Surface culture inadequate
Decubiti	None	Swabs are not recommended; Biopsy specimen preferred

References

Brooks GF, Butel JS, Morse SA. *Jawetz, Melnick, & Adelberg's Medical Microbiology*. 24th ed. New York: Appleton-Lange Medical Books/McGraw-Hill; 2010.

Forbes B, Sahm DF, Weissfeld AS. *Bailey & Scott's Diagnostic Microbiology*. 12th ed. St. Louis: Mosby-Yearbook/Harcourt Health Sciences; 2007.

Gilbert DN, Moellering RC, Eliopoulos GM, Chambers HF, Saag MS. *The Sanford Guide to Antimicrobial Therapy 2011*. 41st ed. Sperryville, VA: Antimicrobial Therapy, Inc.; 2011.

Grota P, ed. *APIC Text of Infection Control and Epidemiology*, 4th ed. Washington, DC: Association for Professionals in Infection Control and Epidemiology, 2014.

Heymann DL, ed. *Control of Communicable Diseases Manual*, 19th ed. Baltimore: American Public Health Association, United Book Press, Inc.; 2008.

Mahon CR, Lehman, DC, Manuselis G, eds. *Textbook of Diagnostic Microbiology*, 4th ed. St. Louis: W.B. Saunders Company/Harcourt Health Sciences; 2010.

Mandell GL, Bennett JE, Dolin R, eds. *Principles and Practice of Infectious Diseases*, 7th ed. St. Louis: Churchill Livingstone/Harcourt Health Sciences; 2010.

Pickering LK, ed. *2009 Red Book, Report of the Committee on Infectious Diseases*, 28th ed. Elk Grove: American Academy of Pediatrics; 2009.

Porter, RS and Kaplan, JL, eds. *The Merck Manual of Diagnosis and Therapy*, 19th ed. Whitehouse Station: Merck & Company; 2011.

Tortora GJ, Funke BR, Case CL. *Microbiology, An Introduction*, 10th ed. San Francisco: Benjamin Cummings Publishing; 2009.

Versalovic J, Carroll KC, Jorgensen JH, Funke G, Landry ML, Warnock DW, eds. *Manual of Clinical Microbiology*, 12th ed. Washington, DC: American Society of Microbiology Press; 2011.

Additional Resources

APIC Text Online. 2011. http://text.apic.org/

American Society for Microbiology. http://www.asm.org

Centers for Disease Control and Prevention. http://www.cdc.gov

Emerging & Re-emerging Infectious Diseases. In: NIH Education, Understanding Infectious Diseases. Available at http://science.education.nih.gov/supplements/nih1/diseases/guide/understanding1.htm Accessed 1/4/2012.

Health-care Associated Infections. http://www.cdc.gov/hai/

The Sanford Guide to Antimicrobial Therapy 41st edition, 2011. http://www.sanfordguide.com

World Health Organization. http://www.who.int

Chapter Six

————

Bioterrorism Agents

Bioterrorism is defined as the unlawful use, or threatened use, of bacteria, viruses, or toxins to produce death or disease in humans. The act is intended to create fear and to intimidate. Biological warfare agents have been used for more than 2,000 years.

- During the 6th century, B.C., Assyrians poisoned enemy wells with fungus.
- In 1346, the Tartar army hurled bodies of soldiers who died during plague outbreaks over city walls, beginning the "Black Death" pandemic in Europe.
- In 1756, the English provided smallpox-laden blankets to Native Americans who were loyal to the French during the French-Indian War.
- In 1937, Japan used human test subjects in occupied China. Seven hundred and thirty-one out of 1,000 autopsies revealed death by aerosolized anthrax.
- In 1940, Japanese planes dropped pots containing plague-infected fleas over China.
- In 2001, bioterrorism attacks using anthrax-laden letters occurred in the United States.

The Centers for Disease Control (CDC) categorize bioterrorism agents according to priority. These agents include:

Category A agents are biological agents that have high potential for adverse public health impact, increased risk to national security, serious potential for large-scale dissemination, potential for public panic and social disruption, and high mortality rates.

Category A bioterrorism agents include:

- Anthrax (*Bacillus anthracis*)
- Botulism (*Clostridium botulinum* toxin)
- Plague (*Yersinia pestis*)
- Smallpox (Variola major)

- Tularemia (*Francisella tularensis*)
- Viral hemorrhagic fevers
  - Filoviruses
    - ∘ Ebola hemorrhagic fever (Ebola virus)
    - ∘ Marburg hemorrhagic fever (Marburg virus)
  - Arenaviruses
    - ∘ Argentinian hemorrhagic fever (Junin virus)
    - ∘ Bolivian hemorrhagic fever (Machupo virus)
    - ∘ Lassa fever (Lassa virus)

Category B agents have moderate ease in disseminating, specific require-ments for disease surveillance, moderate morbidity rates, and low mortality rates.

Category B bioterrorism agents include:

- Brucellosis (*Brucella* spp.)
- Epsilon toxin (*Clostridium perfringens*)
- Glanders (*Burkholderia mallei*)
- Melioidosis (*Burkholderia pseudomallei*)
- Psittacosis (*Chlamydia psittaci*)
- Q fever (*Coxiella burnetii*)
- Ricin toxin from *Ricinus communis* (castor beans)
- *Staphylococcal* enterotoxin B
- Typhus (*Rickettsia prowazekii*)
- Alpha viruses
  - Eastern and western equine encephalomyelitis viruses (Eastern equine encephalitis {EEE}, Western equine encephalitis {WEE})
  - Venezuelan equine encephalomyelitis virus (VEE)

  Subset of Category B agents include food or waterborne pathogens, such as:
  - *Cryptosporidium parvum*
  - *Escheria coli* O157:H7
  - *Salmonella* species
  - *Shigella dysenteriae*
  - *Vibrio cholera*

Category C agents are pathogens that potentially could be engineered for mass dissemination due to availability, due to ease of production, resulting in major health impact, and with potential for high morbidity or mortality rates.

Category C agents include:

- Hantavirus
- Nipah virus
- Multidrug-resistant tuberculosis
- Tickborne encephalitis viruses
- Tickborne hemorrhagic fever viruses
- Yellow fever
- Influenza (pandemic)

Table

The following table provides basic concepts regarding prevention of health-care-associated infections once an outbreak due to a bioterrorism agent has been identified. The table includes:

- Microbes (bacteria, parasite, and virus), including CDC category, that are considered bioterrorism agents
- Diseases or common names of the bioterrorism agents
- Precautions and treatment to prevent healthcare-associated infections once an outbreak has been identified

Information regarding genus, description, name, infections and mode of transmission will not be duplicated in this chapter. The reader is encouraged to refer to the Bacteria, Parasites and Viruses Chapters.

Microbe	Disease Name	CDC Category	Issues related to Healthcare-associated Transmission	Treatment	Comments
Bacteria					
Bacillus anthracis	anthrax	A	Inhalation - Standard Precautions; Not transmitted person to person. Cutaneous - Standard and Contact Precautions; Direct contact with skin lesions MAY result in cutaneous infection. GI - Standard Precautions; Not transmitted person to person; No restrictions on room placement or transportation	Vaccine used in US military, not offered to general public; Ciprofloxacin - drug of choice; Doxycycline and/or penicillin may also be used	Spores weaponized into powder for inhalation as bioterrorism agent
Burkholderia mallei	glanders	B	Standard and Airborne Precautions; N95 mask required for all entering the room; Private room; Limit movement from room to essential purposes only; During transport, place mask on patient	Limited antibiotic treatment information exists; Ceftazidime, cotrimoxazole may be used	Exists only in infected susceptible hosts (horses, mules, donkeys); Endemic in Africa, Asia, Middle East, Central and South America
Burkholderia pseudomallei	melioidosis	B	Standard and Airborne Precautions; N95 mask required for all entering the room; Private room; Limit movement from room to essential purposes only; During transport, place mask on patient	Limited antibiotic treatment information exists; Ceftazidime, cotrimoxazole may be used	Widely distributed in soil and water of the tropics; Endemic in Southeast Asia and Northern Australia
Brucella	brucellosis, "Malta fever," undulant fever	B	Standard and Contact Precautions; Private room; Limit movement from room to essential purposes only	Rifampin, streptomycin, doxycycline	Majority of cases from consumption of unpasteurized dairy products
Chlamydiophila psittaci	psittacosis	B	Standard Precautions; No restrictions regarding room placement nor movement within the hospital	Tetracycline, erythromycin	Widespread dissemination possible to people with pet birds, visit pet shops, and/or care for birds

Organism	Disease/Toxin	Category	Precautions	Treatment	Notes
Clostridium botulinum toxin	botulism	A	Standard Precautions; Not transmitted by person to person contact; No restrictions on room placement nor movement within the hospital	CDC currently investigating use of 7 different botulism toxins for vaccination; Supportive treatment, equine antitoxin, and ventilatory support; Avoid clindamycin and aminogylcosides	One of deadliest toxins known; Characterized by the 4 "Ds": diplopia, dysarthria, dysphonia, and dysphagia
Clostridium perfringens	epsilon toxin	B	Standard and Contact Precautions; Private room	Fluid and electrolyte replacement	Spores germinate and multiply in foods prepared in large quantities (banquets, schools, camps, food caterers, restaurants) and kept warm for prolonged periods; Epsilon toxin produced by spores in lower intestines cause symptoms
Coxiella burnetii	Q fever	B	Standard Precautions; No restrictions regarding room placement nor movement within the hospital	Tetracycline or doxycycline	Major manifestations of chronic disease are endocarditis and hepatitis; Patients with endocarditis mortality rate 30-60%
Escherichia coli	E. coli 0157:H7	B	Standard and Contact Precautions; Private room	Fluid and electrolyte replacement; Transfusions and hemodialysis may be necessary; Role of antibiotic therapy uncertain	Hemolytic uremic syndrome (HUS): Triad of microangiopathic hemolytic anemia, thrombocytopenia, acute renal dysfunction; Frequency 5-10%

(continued)

Bacteria (continued)

Microbe	Disease Name	CDC Category	Issues related to Nosocomial Transmission	Treatment	Comments
Francisella tularensis	tularemia	A	Standard Precautions; Not transmitted by person to person contact; No restrictions on room placement nor movement within the hospital	Streptomycin or gentamicin; Post exposure treatment - doxycycline or ciprofloxacin; No vaccine available	Experimental attenuated strain available from USAMRIID (U.S. Army Medical Research Institute for Infectious Diseases); Highly infective nature and ease of aerosolization can be widely produced as bioterrorism agent; Generally non-lethal; Severely incapacitating
Mycobacterium tuberculosis	multidrug-resistant tuberculosis (MDR-TB)	C	Airborne Precautions; N95 mask required for all entering the room; Private room with anteroom; Limit movement from room to essential purposes only; During transport, place mask on patient	Complex and challenging; Second-line drugs include aminoglycosides (kanamycin and amikacin), cycloserine, terizidone, ethionamide, prothionamide, capreomycin, aminosalicylic acid, and fluoroquinolones (including ofloxacin, levofloxacin, gatifloxacin, and moxifloxacin); Percentage of patients with MDR-TB who are cured is estimated to be no more than 69%, even when treated for more than 18 months with directly observed treatment	MDR-TB is resistant to isoniazid and rifampin, with or without resistance to other drugs; Extremely resistant tuberculosis is resistant to isoniazid and rifampin, among first-line anti-TB drugs, any fluoroquinolone, and at least one second-line injectable drug (amikacin, capreomycin, or kanamycin)
Rickettsia prowazekii	typhus	B	Standard Precautions; No restrictions regarding room placement nor movement within the hospital	Tetracycline, chloramphenicol, doxycycline	Cream and gel pediculocides (pyrethrins, lindane) for delousing; Excessive doses of topical lindane can cause seizures in children

Organism	Category	Disease	Precautions	Treatment	Notes
Salmonella spp.	B	salmonellosis	Standard and Contact Precautions; Private room; Limit movement from room to essential purposes only	Ciprofloxacin, ampicillin, amoxicillin, chloramphenicol; Fluid and electrolyte replacement	*Salmonella* spp., discovered by American scientist named Salmon; Known to cause illness for over 100 years; Approximately 40,000 cases of salmonellosis reported yearly in U.S.
Salmonella typhi	B	typhoid fever	Standard and Contact Precautions; Private room; Limit movement from room to essential purposes only	Chloramphenicol, amoxicillin, quinolones; supportive care	Typhoid vaccine available from CDC
Staphylococcus aureus	B	enterotoxin B	Standard and Contact Precautions; Private room; Limit movement from room to essential purposes only	Fluid and electrolyte replacement	Toxic Shock Syndrome (TSS), food poisoning; Short incubation period of 30 minutes to 7 hours
Shigella dysenteriae	B	shigellosis; dysentery	Standard and Contact Precautions; Private room; Limit movement from room to essential purposes only	Ciprofloxacin, ampicillin, amoxicillin, chloramphenicol; Fluid and electrolyte replacement	Hemolytic Uremic Syndrome (HUS); Colonic perforation; Fulminant toxic encephalopathy (ekiri syndrome) can be lethal within 48 hours of onset; Rare in U.S.; Widespread in African and Indian subcontinents
Yersinia pestis	A	plague	Pneumonic - Standard and Droplet Precautions; Mask protection, preferably N-95 masks, are mandatory for patients and close contacts; Highly contagious; Spreads by respiratory droplets; Private room or cohort with like patient; Restrict movement to essential purposes only / Bubonic - Standard Precautions	Streptomycin or gentamicin; doxycycline or ciprofloxacin; chloramphenicol for plague meningitis	Droplet Precautions mandatory for first 48 hours of antibiotic treatment; Acral gangrene may be late complication of pneumonic plague and may occur in fingers, toes, earlobes, nose and penis
Vibrio cholerae	B	cholera	Standard and Contact Precautions; Private room or cohort with like patients when private room unavailable; Limit movement to essential purposes only	Tetracycline, doxycycline; Rapid rehydration and electrolyte replacement	Epidemic in Africa, Asia, Latin America; Typical stools: colorless, with small flecks of mucus, called "rice water"

(continued)

Microbe	Disease Name	CDC Category	Issues related to Nosocomial Transmission	Treatment	Comments
Other (Non microbe)					
Ricinus communis (caster beans)	Ricin toxin	B	Standard Precautions; Not transmitted by person to person contact; No restrictions on room placement nor movement within the hospital; intensive care unit maybe required for ventilatory support	Supportive treatment to minimize poison effects; no antidote; Death occurs within 36-72 hours, depending on route of exposure (inhalation, ingestion, or injection) and amount of inoculum	Ricin is part of the waste "mash" produced when castor oil is made; Ingestion symptoms, vomiting, bloody diarrhea, may occur within 6 hours and leads to multiorgan failure and death; Inhalation symptoms may occur within 8 hours lead to respiratory failure, multiorgan failure and death; Exposure occurs via ingestion of food, water; inhalation; injection (poison ricin pellet)
Parasite					
Cryptosporidium parvum	commonly known as "Crypto."	B	Standard Precautions; Strict hand hygiene	Prevent dehydration; Rapid loss of fluids from diarrhea may be life threatening to infants; Nitazoxanide has been FDA-approved for treatment of diarrhea in people with healthy immune systems, effectiveness in immunosuppressed individuals is unclear.	Spread directly from person-to-person, through contact with feces-contaminated objects (e.g. toys), or by swallowing contaminated food or water (drinking and recreational) or food. Crypto outbreaks in child care settings are most common during late summer/early fall (August/September); Chlorinated recreational water venue (i.e. swimming pool, water park, water play area, splash pad, spray pad) may not provide protection from exposure, Cryptosporidium is chlorine-resistant and can live for days in chlorine-treated water.

Viruses

Hantavirus	hantavirus hemorrhagic fever, Four Corners virus, hantavirus pulmonary syndrome	C	Standard Precautions; No restrictions regarding room placement nor movement within the hospital	Supportive treatment for shock and renal failure; Prevent over-hydration; Ribavirin may benefit hemorrhagic fever	Transmission occurs via aerosol transmission from rodent excreta
Influenza virus	Pandemic influenza (Types - Swine - H1N1; Avian - H5N1)	C	Standard, Contact, Airborne. Droplet Precautions; Respiratory Hygiene/ Cough Etiquette; Cohort patients with confirmed or suspected influenza	Use of antiviral drugs for treatment and chemoprophylaxis is key; Adamantanes and neuraminidase inhibitors used successfully to control outbreaks caused by susceptible strains; If an emerging public health threat is identified for which no licensed or approved product exists, the Project BioShield Act of 2004 authorizes the FDA Commissioner to issue an EUA so appropriate countermeasures (e.g. distribution of unlicensed antiviral medications) can be taken quickly to protect the safety of the U.S. population. CDC in conjunction with NIH provides expert consultation to the FDA Commissioner regarding the appropriateness of EUA requests and supports the distribution of products stored in the Strategic National Stockpile (SNS) formulary	During outbreak, re-offer influenza vaccination (if available) to unvaccinated staff and patients; Restrict staff movement between wards or buildings; Restrict contact between ill staff or visitors and patients

(continued)

Microbe	Disease Name	CDC Category	Issues related to Nosocomial Transmission	Treatment	Comments
Viruses (continued)					
Nipah virus	nipah virus encephalitis	C	Standard Precautions; No restrictions regarding room placement nor movement within the hospital	Supportive treatment for shock and renal failure; Prevent over-hydration; Ribavirin may benefit hemorrhagic fever	First isolated in 1999 - encephalitis and respiratory illness outbreak in adult men in Malaysia and Singapore
Variola major virus	smallpox	A	Standard, Airborne, and Contact Precautions; Must be isolated immediately; N-95 masks are required for patients and close contacts; Highly contagious; Negative pressure room with door closed at all times; If transportation essential, place mask on patient	Vaccina (Cowpox virus) - live virus - early vaccination critical; Cidofovir (antiviral) may be offered under FDA Investigational new drug protocol	Dangerous due to highly contagious nature of infected persons and their pox; Occurs only in humans with no external hosts or vectors
Yellow fever virus	yellow fever	C	Standard Precautions; No restrictions regarding room placement nor movement within the hospital	Supportive treatment for symptoms; Vaccination can prevent yellow fever	Three transmission cycles: 1. Sylvatic (jungle) – tropical rainforests, virus transmitted by mosquitoes from monkeys to humans, majority of infections occur in young men (loggers) working in the jungle. 2. Savannah (intermediate) – humid or semi-humid areas of Africa, virus transmitted from mosquitoes to humans; most common type of outbreak in Africa. 3. Urban-transmission of virus via *Aedes aegypti* mosquito; virus brought to urban setting via viremic human who was infected in the jungle or savannah cycle results in large explosive epidemics

Viral encephalitis viruses

Eastern equine encephalitis virus	Eastern equine encephalitis (EEE)	B	Standard Precautions; No restrictions regarding room placement nor movement within the hospital	Supportive treatment	Common in Eastern U.S.; One of most severe mosquito-borne viral infections: Encephalitic disease >5%, Mortality rate >50%
Western equine encephalitis virus	Western equine encephalitis (WEE)	B	Standard Precautions; No restrictions regarding room placement nor movement within the hospital	Supportive treatment	Primarily limited to North America; Encephalitis rate higher in children; Increased morbidity mainly confined to infants; < 700 cases in U.S. since 1964
Venezuelan equine encephalitis virus	Venezuelan equine encephalitis (VEE)	B	Standard Precautions; No restrictions regarding room placement nor movement within the hospital	Supportive treatment	Primarily in South/Central America; Encephalitis rates higher among children

Tick-borne encephalitis viruses

Three tick-borne encephalitis virus subtypes: European or Western Far Eastern Siberian	Tick-borne encephalitis (TBE)	C	Standard Precautions; No restrictions regarding room placement nor movement within the hospital	Supportive treatment; anti-inflammatory drugs; ventilatory support may be necessary	TBE-important infectious disease in many parts of Europe, Russia, Asia; Dependent on *ixodid* tick reservoir; 10-20% of infected patients have long-lasting or permanent neuropsychiatric sequelae

(continued)

Viral hemorrhagic viruses

Arenaviruses

Microbe	Disease Name	CDC Category	Issues related to Nosocomial Transmission	Treatment	Comments
Junin virus	Argentinian hemorrhagic fever	A	Standard and Contact Precautions; Private room or cohort with like patients when private room unavailable	Supportive treatment; Convalescent-phase plasma has been used with success in some patients; Vaccine available	First reported in 1958; Endemic to Argentina; Transmission occurs via a small rodent, known as the maize mouse (*Calomys musculinus*) through its saliva and urine via contact of skin or mucous membranes, or through inhalation of infected particles; Common in people who reside or work in rural areas; 80% of those infected are males between 15 and 60 years of age
Lassa virus	Lassa fever	A	Standard, Airborne, and Contact Precautions; Private room with anteroom preferred or Intensive Care Unit; Quarantine required. Personal protective equipment needed: N-95 or powered air-purifying respirators (PAPRs); Face shields, double gloves, goggles, impermeable gowns, and shoe covers; Highly transmissible via contact and droplet exposure from blood and body fluids	Ribavirin; Supportive treatment	First described in 1950; Virus identified in 1969 when 2 missionary nurses died in Lassa, Nigeria; Endemic in Guinea, Liberia, Sierra Leona, parts of Nigeria

Machupo virus	Bolivian hemorrhagic fever	A	Standard, Airborne, and Contact Precautions; Private room with anteroom preferred or Intensive Care Unit; Quarantine required. Personal protective equipment needed: N-95 or powered air-purifying respirators (PAPRs); Face shields, double gloves, goggles, impermeable gowns, and shoe covers; Highly transmissible via contact and droplet exposure from blood and body fluids	Ribavirin; Supportive treatment	Also known as black typhus; Occurs primarily in Bolivia; First identified in 1959; No cases identified between 1973 and 1994; Genetically related Junin virus vaccine may be an effective prophylactic measure

Filoviruses

Ebola virus; sub types Zaïre, Sudan, Côte d'Ivoire	African hemorrhagic fever, Ebola hemorrhagic fever	A	Standard, Airborne, and Contact Precautions; Private room with anteroom preferred or Intensive Care Unit; Quarantine required. Personal protective equipment needed: N-95 or powered air-purifying respirators (PAPRs); Face shields, double gloves, goggles, impermeable gowns, and shoe covers; Highly transmissible via contact and droplet exposure from blood and body fluids	Ribavirin; Supportive treatment; Fluid replacement; Vaccines in early stages of development	More than 10 strains; 50-90% mortality rate; Death results from multiple organ failure and hypovolemic shock
Marburg virus	Marburg hemorrhagic fever	A	Standard, Airborne, and Contact Precautions; Private room with anteroom preferred or Intensive Care Unit; Quarantine required. Personal protective equipment needed: N-95 or powered air-purifying respirators (PAPRs); Face shields, double gloves, goggles, impermeable gowns, and shoe covers; Highly transmissible via contact and droplet exposure from blood and body fluids	Ribavirin; Supportive treatment; Fluid replacement; Vaccines in early stages of development	Discovered in Marburg, Germany; 25-100% mortality rate

(continued)

Tick-borne hemorrhagic fever viruses

Microbe	Disease Name	CDC Category	Issues related to Nosocomial Transmission	Treatment	Comments
Nairovirus	Crimean-Congo hemorrhagic fever	C	Standard and Contact Precautions; Avoid exposure to blood and body fluids	Supportive care; Antiviral drug ribavirin with some benefit	First seen in Crimea in 1944; Recognized in the Congo in 1969; Nairovirus infection found in Eastern Europe, Mediterranean, Northwestern China, Central Asia, Southern Europe, Africa, Middle East, India; Transmission occurs via contact with infected animal blood, ticks or improperly sterilized medical equipment, contaminated medical supplies
Flavivirus Kyasanur forest disease virus	Kyasanur Forest disease	C	Standard and Contact Precautions	Supportive treatment; Fluid replacement	Identified in 1957 when isolated from tick-infected monkey from Kyasanur Forest in India; Infections seasonally transmitted in Southern and Central India and Siberia; Occurs among villagers and lumbermen with forest contact
Flavivirus Omsk hemorrhagic fever virus	Omsk hemorrhagic fever	C	Standard and Contact Precautions	Supportive treatment; Fluid replacement	First described between 1945 and 1947 in Omsk, Russia; Infections seasonally transmitted in Southern and Central India and Siberia via tick-infected muskrats

References

Gilbert DN, Moellering RC, Eliopoulos GM, Chambers HF, Saag MS. *The Sanford Guide to Antimicrobial Therapy 2011*. 41st ed. Sperryville, VA: Antimicrobial Therapy, Inc.; 2011.

Grota P, ed. *APIC Text of Infection Control and Epidemiology*, 4th ed. Washington, DC: Association for Professionals in Infection Control and Epidemiology, 2014.

Heymann DL, ed. *Control of Communicable Diseases Manual*, 19th ed. Baltimore: American Public Health Association, United Book Press, Inc.; 2008.

Mahon CR, Lehman, DC, Manuselis G, eds. *Textbook of Diagnostic Microbiology*, 4th ed. St. Louis: W.B. Saunders Company/Harcourt Health Sciences; 2010.

Mandell GL, Bennett JE, Dolin R, eds. *Principles and Practice of Infectious Diseases*, 7th ed. St. Louis: Churchill Livingstone/Harcourt Health Sciences; 2010.

Pickering LK, ed. *2009 Red Book, Report of the Committee on Infectious Diseases*, 28th ed. Elk Grove: American Academy of Pediatrics; 2009.

Porter, RS and Kaplan, JL, eds. *The Merck Manual of Diagnosis and Therapy*, 19th ed. Whitehouse Station: Merck & Company; 2011.

Tortora GJ, Funke BR, Case CL. *Microbiology, An Introduction*, 10th ed. San Francisco: Benjamin Cummings Publishing; 2009.

Versalovic J, Carroll KC, Jorgensen JH, Funke G, Landry ML, Warnock DW, eds. *Manual of Clinical Microbiology*, 12th ed. Washington, DC: American Society of Microbiology Press; 2011.

Additional Resources

APIC Text Online. 2011. http://text.apic.org/

American Society for Microbiology. http://www.asm.org

Biological warfare. In: Wikipedia. Available at http://en.wikipedia.org/wiki/Biological_warfare. Accessed 2/14/2012.

Bioterrorism. In: Wikipedia. Available at http://en.wikipedia.org/wiki/Bio-terrorism. Accessed 2/14/2012.

Centers for Disease Control and Prevention. http://www.cdc.gov

CDC Bioterrorism Agents/Diseases by Category. In: Emergency Prepared-ness & Response. Available at http://emergency.cdc.gov/agent/agentlist-cate-gory.asp. Accessed 2/14/2012.

Crimean-Congo Hemorrhagic Fever. In: CDC Special Pathogens Branch. Available at http://www.cdc.gov/ncidod/dvrd/spb/mnpages/dispages/cchf.htm. Accessed 2/17/2012.

Crisis and Emergency Risk Communication Course (CERC). In: Pandemic Influenza Overview & Objectives. Available at http://emergency.cdc.gov/cerc/panflu/overview.asp. Accessed 2/16/2012.

Disease Information for Tick-borne hemorrhagic fevers. In: DiagnosisPro. Available at http://en.diagnosispro.com/disease_information-for/tick-borne-hemorrhagic-fevers/20416. Accessed 2/17/2012.

Emerging & Re-emerging Infectious Diseases. In: NIH Education, Under-standing Infectious Diseases. Available at http://science.education.nih.gov/supplements/nih1/diseases/guide/understanding1.htm Accessed 1/4/2012.

Facts about Ricin. In: CDC Emergency Preparedness and Response. Available at http://emergency.cdc.gov/agent/ricin/facts.asp. Accessed 2/14/2012.

Haemorrhagic fevers, Viral. In: Health Topics, World Health Organization (WHO). Available at http://www.who.int/topics/haemorrhagic_fevers_viral/en/index.html. Accessed 2/16/2012.

Influenza Type A Viruses and Subtypes. In: CDC Seasonal Influenza (Flu). Available at http://www.cdc.gov/flu/avianflu/influenza-a-virus-subtypes.htm. Accessed 2/16/2012.

Information on H3N2 Variant Influenza A Viruses. In: CDC Seasonal Influ-enza (Flu). Available at http://www.cdc.gov/flu/swineflu/influenza-variant-viruses-h3n2v.htm. Accessed 3/9/2012.

Omsk Hemorrhagic Fever. In: CDC Special Pathogens Branch. Available at http://www.cdc.gov/ncidod/dvrd/spb/mnpages/dispages/omsk.htm. Accessed 2/17/2012.

SHEA Guidelines and Resources. Compendium of Strategies to Prevent HAIs. Available at http://www.shea-online.org/GuidelinesResources/CompendiumofStrategiestoPreventHAIs.aspx

The Sanford Guide to Antimicrobial Therapy 41st edition, 2011. http://www.sanfordguide.com

Tick-borne Encephalitis. In: CDC Special Pathogens Branch. Available at http://www.cdc.gov/ncidod/dvrd/spb/mnpages/dispages/TBE.htm. Accessed 2/16/2012.

Top Priority Bioterrorism Threat Agents. In: Bioterrorism Information, John Hopkins Medicine. Available at http://www.hopkinsmedicine.org/heic/bioterrorism/agents.html. Accessed 2/8/2012.

Viral Hemorrhagic Fevers. In: CDC Special Pathogens Branch. Available at http://www.cdc.gov/ncidod/dvrd/spb/mnpages/dispages/vhf.htm. Accessed 2/16/2012.

Viral Hemorrhagic Fever Information. In: Bioterrorism Information, John Hopkins Medicine. Available at http://www.hopkinsmedicine.org/heic/bioterrorism/facts/vhf.html. Accessed 2/16/2012.

Yellow Fever. In: CDC – Yellow Fever. Available at http://www.cdc.gov/yellowfever/. Accessed 2/16/2012.

Yellow fever. In: WHO Global Alert and Response (GAR). Available at http://www.who.int/csr/disease/yellowfev/en/index.html. http://www.who.int/topics/yellow_fever/en/index.html. Accessed 2/16/2012.

Yellow fever. In: WHO Media centre. Available at http://www.who.int/mediacentre/factsheets/fs100/en/. Accessed 2/16/2012.

World Health Organization. http://www.who.int

Chapter Seven

Antimicrobial Therapy

Antimicrobials encompass a wide variety of pharmaceutical agents that include antibacterial, antifungal, antiparasitic, and antiviral drugs. Antimicrobials are:

- Bactericidal – cause death and disruption of the bacterial cell. Examples include:
  - B-lactams primarily act on the cell wall
  - Daptomycin acts on the cell membrane
  - Fluoroquinolones act on bacterial DNA
- Bacteriostatic – inhibit bacterial replication without killing the organism. Examples include:
  - Sulfonamides
  - Tetracyclines
  - Macrolides which inhibit protein synthesis

Whether an antimicrobial is bactericidal or bacteriostatic depends on the concentration to which the microbe is exposed.

Mechanisms of Antimicrobial Action

Mechanism	Antimicrobial(s)
Cell wall or membrane synthesis inhibition	B-lactams (penicillins, cephalosporins, monobactams, carbapenems) Glycopeptide (vancomycin) Echinocandins (caspofungin) Daptomycin, colistimethate Antifungal (fluconazole)
Protein synthesis in the bacterial ribosome inhibition	Aminoglycosides (gentamicin, tobramycin) Macrolides (azithromycin) Tetracyclines Oxazolidinone (linezolid)
Essential metabolites production (metabolic pathway) inhibition	Trimethoprim-sulfamethoxazole Ethambutol
Nucleic acid synthesis inhibition	Fluoroquinolones (ciprofloxacin, levofloxacin, moxifloxacin) Antifungal (flucytosine) Antivirals (acyclovir)

Synergistic Activity

Synergy is the combined effect of antimicrobials that is greater than the sum of their independent antimicrobial activities when measured separately. The combination of particular B-lactams and aminoglycosides exhibits synergistic activity against a variety of Gram-positive and Gram-negative microbes. Treating endocarditis caused by *Enterococcus* species with a combination of penicillin (alone is bacteriostatic) and gentamicin (alone has no significant activity) provides rapid bactericidal synergistic activity. Endocarditis caused by viridans group *Streptococci* can be treated more effectively for two weeks with penicillin or ceftriaxone with gentamicin than for four weeks of penicillin or ceftriaxone alone.

Antimicrobial Indications

Antimicrobial therapy can be categorized by type of use including:

- Microbe (Pathogen)-directed:
  - Pathogen has been identified by tests, including culture, serology, polymerase chain reaction (PCR)
  - Narrowest spectrum antimicrobial is used to decrease emergence of antimicrobial resistance and superinfection
- Empirical:
  - Gram stain suggests causative pathogen
  - Clinical picture, such as site of infection, microbes that colonize the site, prior screening for MRSA, other host factors, and local bacterial resistance patterns or antibiograms provide an indication of likely pathogens
  - Broad spectrum antimicrobials are used due to uncertainty of pathogen
- Prophylaxis
  - Antimicrobials used to prevent infection
  - Surgical antimicrobial prophylaxis is most common
  - Single dose of a cephalosporin, such as cefazolin, administered within one hour of initial incision targets most likely microbes (common commensals)

Antimicrobial Resistance

Widespread antimicrobial use is the main selective pressure responsible for increasing resistance in community and healthcare facilities. Resistance mechanisms include:

- Antimicrobial inactivation
  - Bacteria produce enzymes that can destroy or inactivate antimicrobials.
  - Bacteria may produce B-lactamase enzymes that destroy penicillins and cephalosporins.

- Target site alteration
  - The binding site of the antimicrobial on the pathogen is altered.
- Permeability or efflux decrease
  - Resistance develops due to a change in drug permeability.
- Metabolic pathway bypass
  - Bacteria develop alternative pathways to bypass the metabolic pathway inhibited by the antimicrobial.
- Point mutations in existing genes
  - Random errors occur during DNA replication.
- New gene acquisition
  - Antimicrobial resistance requires complex structural or enzymatic changes resulting in new resistant genes.

Common Antimicrobial Misuses

- Prolonged empiric antimicrobial therapy without clear evidence of infection
- Treating a positive clinical culture in the absence of infection
- Failure to narrow antimicrobial therapy after a causative pathogen is identified
- Prolonged prophylaxis
- Excessive use of certain antimicrobials, such as fluoroquinolones led to fluoroquinolone resistant strain of *C. difficile*

Table

The following table presents general information for an understanding of the major classifications and broad categories of antimicrobials. Note that the table lists:

- antimicrobial classes
- antimicrobial subclasses
- representative antimicrobials
- effective antimicrobial activity for bacteria, fungi, viruses, parasites

The reader is encouraged to refer to the most recent edition of the Sanford Guide and the Medical Newsletter regarding specific antimicrobial therapy per pathogen, body site, and/or infection. Evidence-based practice guidelines for specific infectious disease syndromes and infections caused by specific microbes are available from the Infectious Diseases Society of America website: http://www.idsociety.org/Content.aspx?id=9088

Antibacterials			
Class	Subclass	Representative Antimicrobial	Antimicrobial Activity
Beta-lactams			
Pencillins	Natural penicillin	Penicillin G	Bactericidal; Inhibits cell wall synthesis; Gram-positive bacteria, including *Enterococci*, most *Streptococci*, and oral anaerobic microbes; Drug of choice for group A *Streptococcus* pharyngitis
	Aminopenicillins	Ampicillin Amoxicillin	Inhibits cell wall synthesis; Gram-negative bacteria (*E. coli* and *H. influenzae*); Retained natural penicillins antimicrobial activity
	Penicillinase-resistant penicillins	Cloxacillin Nafcillin Ticarcillin Dicloxacillin Piperacillin	Inhibits cell wall synthesis; Gram-positive bacteria; Gram-negative bacteria, including *Pseudomonas*; Retained natural penicillins antimicrobial activity
	Penicillinase-resistant penicillins with beta-lactamase inhibitors added	Amoxicillin-clavulanate (Augmentin) Ampicillin-sulbactam (Unasyn) Piperacillin-tazobactam (Zosyn) Ticarcillin-clavulanate	Inhibits B-lactamases' enzymes; Retained natural penicillins antimicrobial activity; Broaden activity anaerobic bacteria; Methicillin-susceptible *Staphylococci* (MSSA; Gram-negative bacteria other than *Pseudomonas*
Cephalosporins	First generation	Cefazolin (Ancef) Cephalexin (Keflex)	Interferes with cell wall synthesis; Gram-positive and Gram-negative bacteria, including most strains of *E. coli, Klebsiella pneumoniae, Proteus mirabilis*; Spectrum varies by antimicrobial
	Second generation	Cefuroxime (Zinacef) Cefotetan Cefoxitin (Mefoxin)	Interferes with cell wall synthesis; Gram-positive and Gram-negative bacteria; Increased antimicrobial activity against enteric Gram-negative bacilli, *Neisseria* species, *H. influenzae*; Spectrum varies by antimicrobial
	Third generation	Ceftriaxone (Rocephin) Cefoperazone (Cefobid) Cefotaxime (Claforan) Ceftazidime (Fortaz) Ceftizoxime (Cefizox)	Interferes with cell wall synthesis; Gram-positive and Gram-negative bacteria; Enhanced antimicrobial activity against Gram-negative bacilli; Spectrum varies by antimicrobial; Increase in resistant *Streptococcus pneumoniae* limits empirical therapy

(continued)

Class	Subclass	Representative Antimicrobial	Antimicrobial Activity
	Fourth generation	Cefepime (Maxipime)	Interferes with cell wall synthesis; Broad spectrum antimicrobial activity against Gram-positive bacteria, including *Pseudomonas* species and Gram-negative bacteria; Does not cover MRSA nor anaerobic bacteria lung, abdominal, soft tissue infections
		Ceftaroline (Teflaro)	Interferes with cell wall synthesis; First B-lactam approved for treatment of MRSA; Gram-positive and Gram-negative bacteria; Penicillin-resistant *Streptococcus pneumoniae*, *Klebsiella* species; *E. coli*; Skin, soft tissue infections, community-acquired pneumonia
Other B-Lactams	Monobactam	Aztreonam	Interferes with cell wall synthesis; Limited to aerobic, Gram-negative bacilli, including *Pseudomonas aeruginosa*; Can be given safely to patients with history of serious reactions to penicillins or cephalosporins
	Carbapenems	Imipenem (Primaxin) Meropenem Doripenem Ertapenem	Binds to pencillin-binding proteins of Gram-positive and Gram-negative microbes; Broad spectrum; Wide range of Gram-negative bacilli; *Pseudomonas*, anaerobic bacteria, *Streptococci*, *Staphylococci* except MRSA
Fluoroquinolones			
	Antipseudomonal	Ciprofloxacin (Cipro)	Bactericidal; Inhibits DNA gyrase enzyme; Gram-negative bacilli; Limited antimicrobial activity against *Staphylococci*, anaerobes, *Streptococci*
	Antistreptococcal	Moxifloxacin	Bactericidal; Inhibits DNA gyrase enzyme; Gram-negative bacilli; *Streptococcus pneumoniae*, *Legionella*, anaerobic bacteria
	Antistreptococcal	Levofloxacin	Bactericidal; Inhibits DNA gyrase enzyme; Gram-negative bacilli; *Streptococcus pneumoniae*, *Legionella*, and *Pseudomonas aeruginosa* (Note: resistance is increasing)

(continued)

Class	Subclass	Representative Antimicrobial	Antimicrobial Activity
Other Antibacterials			
	Aminoglycosides	Gentamicin Tobramycin Amikacin Streptomycin	Inhibits bacterial protein synthesis; Used in combination with other antimicrobials for difficult to treat Gram-positive and Gram-negative bacteria; Bactericidal against most aerobic Gram-negative bacteria; Not against anaerobic bacteria
	Chloramphenicol		Inhibits protein synthesis; Gram-positive and Gram-negative bacteria
	Glycopeptide	Vancomycin	Inhibits cell wall and cell membrane synthesis; Bactericidal for *Streptococcus, Enterococcus, Staphylococcus* species; Commonly used for MRSA
	Lipopeptide	Daptomycin	Disrupts cell membrane; Similar to Vancomycin for Gram-positive cocci
	Macrolide-lincos-amides	Erythromycin Azithromycin (Zithromax) Clarithromycin (Biaxin) Clindamycin (Cleocin) Fidaxomicin (Dificid)	Bacteriostatic; Inhibit protein synthesis in ribosome; Macrolides - Erythromycin, Azithromycin, Clarithromycin have limited spectrum for Gram-positive bacteria; Atypical bacteria (*Legionella, Mycoplasma, Chlamydia*); *Helicobacter pylori* gastric/duodenal ulcers; Nontuberculosis *Mycobacteria*; Lincosamide - Clindamycin activity aerobic Gram-positive, anaerobic Gram-positive, Gram-negative bacteria; Dificid: used in treatment of *C. difficile*; inhibits bacterial RNA polymerase
	Nitroimidazole	Metronidazole (Flagyl)	Disrupts cell DNA; Anaerobic microbes; No activity for aerobic microbes; *C. difficile* colitis; parasitic vaginitis (Trichomonas vaginalis); parasitic intestinal infections (*Entamoeba histolytica, Giardia lamblia*)
	Nitrofurantoin	Macrobid Macrodantin	Binds ribosomal proteins; Gram-positive and Gram-negative bacteria
	Oxazolidinones	Linezolid (Zyvox)	Inhibits protein synthesis; Bacteriostatic for Gram-positive microbes; Primary treatment for vancomycin-resistant *Enterococci* (VRE), MRSA

(continued)

Class	Subclass	Representative Antimicrobial	Antimicrobial Activity
	Polymyxins	Colistimethate sodium Colistin sulfate	Targets bacterial cell membrane; Multidrug-resistant microbes – *Pseudomonas aeruginosa, Acinetobacter baumannii* (resistant to all other antimicrobials, including carbapenems and aminoglycosides)
	Rifampicin	Rifampin (Rifadin) Rifabutin Rifaximin	Interferes with nucleic acid synthesis; Prophylaxis for exposure to *Neisseria meningitidis* meningitis; Adjunct therapy for MRSA infected prosthetic device or mechanical valve; Combination (Rifampin/Rifabutin) with other antimicrobials for latent or active *M. tuberculosis*; Rifaximin for *C. difficile* colitis
	Streptogramins	Quinupristin and dalfopristin (Synercid)	Inhibits bacterial protein synthesis; Synergistic combination for vancomycin-resistant *Enterococcus faecium* (VRE) and vancomycin-resistant *Staphylococcus aureus* (VRSA)
	Sulfonamides-Trimethoprim	Trimethoprim/sulfamethoxazole	Synergistic combination; Bactericidal; Inhibits folate synthesis metabolic pathway; *Pneumocystis jirovecii* pneumonia, *Nocardia* species, multidrug-resistant Gram-negative *Stenotrophomonas maltophilia,* unique strains MRSA
	Tetracycline		Inhibits protein synthesis; Gram-positive and Gram-negative bacteria
Antivirals			
Antiretrovirals (HIV treatment)	Nucleoside reverse transcriptase inhibitors	Didanosine Emtricitabine Lamivudine Tenofovir Zidovudine	HAART (highly active antiretroviral therapy) is a combination of various antiretrovirals that suppress viral replication effectively; Commonly used for postexposure prophylaxis of healthcare workers exposed to HIV
	Nonnucleoside reverse transcriptase inhibitors	Delavirdine Efavirenz Nevirapine	HAART (highly active antiretroviral therapy) is a combination of various antiretrovirals that suppress viral replication effectively; Commonly used for postexposure prophylaxis of healthcare workers exposed to HIV

(continued)

Class	Subclass	Representative Antimicrobial	Antimicrobial Activity
	Protease inhibitor	Amprenavir Atazanavir Fosamprenavir Indinavir Nelfinavir Ritonavir	HAART (highly active antiretroviral therapy) is a combination of various antiretrovirals that suppress viral replication effectively; Commonly used for postexposure prophylaxis of healthcare workers exposed to HIV
	Fusion inhibitor	Enfuvirtide	HAART (highly active antiretroviral therapy) is a combination of various antiretrovirals that suppress viral replication effectively; Commonly used for postexposure prophylaxis of healthcare workers exposed to HIV
	Entry inhibitor	Maraviroc	HAART (highly active antiretroviral therapy) is a combination of various antiretrovirals that suppress viral replication effectively; Commonly used for postexposure prophylaxis of healthcare workers exposed to HIV
	Integrase inhibitor	Raltegravir	HAART (highly active antiretroviral therapy) is a combination of various antiretrovirals that suppress viral replication effectively; Commonly used for postexposure prophylaxis of healthcare workers exposed to HIV
Herpesviridae	Herpes simplex	Acyclovir	Herpes zoster; Herpes simplex encephalitis; Acyclovir derivatives (Valaciclovir and Famciclovir) for herpes simplex viruses, type I and II
	Cytomegalovirus (CMV)	Ganciclovir	First line antimicrobial for most CMV infections and life-threatening pneumonitis in solid organ and bone marrow transplants
Influenza	Influenza A and B	Amantadine Rimantadine Zanamivir Oseltamivir	Amantadine and Rimantadine for influenza A; Zanamivir and Oseltamivir (neuraminidase inhibitors) for influenza A and B
Miscellaneous	Respiratory syncytial virus (RSV) Hepatitis C	Ribavirin	Covers wide range of RNA and DNA viruses; Main treatment in combination with Interferon for Hepatitis C

(continued)

Class	Subclass	Representative Antimicrobial	Antimicrobial Activity
	Variety of DNA viruses	Cidofovir	Herpesviruses 6 and 8; Epstein-Barr virus, papillomavirus, polyomavirus, poxvirus, adenovirus
Antifungals			
Azoles	Triazole	Fluconazole Itraconazole (Sporanox)	Candidemia
		Voriconazole Posaconazole	Invasive aspergillosis; Disseminated candidiasis
Polyenes	Nonlipid formulation	Amphotericin B	Weakens fungal cell membrane; *Cryptococci*, histoplasmosis, invasive aspergillosis, other serious yeast or mold infections
	Lipid formulations	Amphotec Abelcet Ambisome	Weakens fungal cell membrane; Less renal/hepatic side effects than Amphotericin B; *Cryptococci*, histoplasmosis, invasive aspergillosis, other serious yeast or mold infections
Other	Echinocandin	Caspofungin Anidulafungin Micafungin	Refractory aspergillosis; Candidiasis; Some invasive candidal infections
	Nucleoside analogue	Flucytosine	Combined with Amphotericin for *Candida* species and *Cryptococcus neoformans*
Antiparasitics			
		Chloroquine Primaquine Mefloquine Doxycycline Quinine	Malaria treatment or prophylaxis
		Praziquanetl	Schistosomiasis
		Ivermectin Albendazole	Nematodes (roundworms)
		Tinidazole	Antiprotozoal; intestinal amebiasis; giardiasis; trichomoniasis
Antimycobacterials		Ethambutol Isoniazid Pyrazinamide Refampin Streptomycin	Agents are usually utilized in combination therapy and not as a single agent treatment

References

Brooks GF, Butel JS, Morse SA. *Jawetz, Melnick, & Adelberg's Medical Microbiology*. 24th ed. New York: Appleton-Lange Medical Books/McGraw-Hill; 2010.

Forbes B, Sahm DF, Weissfeld AS. *Bailey & Scott's Diagnostic Microbiology*. 12th ed. St. Louis: Mosby-Yearbook/Harcourt Health Sciences; 2007.

Gilbert DN, Moellering RC, Eliopoulos GM, Chambers HF, Saag MS. *The Sanford Guide to Antimicrobial Therapy 2011*. 41st ed. Sperryville, VA: Antimicrobial Therapy, Inc.; 2011.

Grota P, ed. *APIC Text of Infection Control and Epidemiology*, 4th ed. Washington, DC: Association for Professionals in Infection Control and Epidemiology, 2014.

Heymann DL, ed. *Control of Communicable Diseases Manual*, 19th ed. Baltimore: American Public Health Association, United Book Press, Inc.; 2008.

Mahon CR, Lehman, DC, Manuselis G, eds. *Textbook of Diagnostic Microbiology*, 4th ed. St. Louis: W.B. Saunders Company/Harcourt Health Sciences; 2010.

Mandell GL, Bennett JE, Dolin R, eds. *Principles and Practice of Infectious Diseases*, 7th ed. St. Louis: Churchill Livingstone/Harcourt Health Sciences; 2010.

Pickering LK, ed. *2009 Red Book, Report of the Committee on Infectious Diseases*, 28th ed. Elk Grove: American Academy of Pediatrics; 2009.

Porter, RS and Kaplan, JL, eds. *The Merck Manual of Diagnosis and Therapy*, 19th ed. Whitehouse Station: Merck & Company; 2011.

Tortora GJ, Funke BR, Case CL. *Microbiology, An Introduction*, 10th ed. San Francisco: Benjamin Cummings Publishing; 2009.

Versalovic J, Carroll KC, Jorgensen JH, Funke G, Landry ML, Warnock DW, eds. *Manual of Clinical Microbiology*, 12th ed. Washington, DC: American Society of Microbiology Press; 2011.

Additional Resources

APIC Text Online. 2011. http://text.apic.org/

American Society for Microbiology. http://www.asm.org

Centers for Disease Control and Prevention. http://www.cdc.gov

Emerging & Re-emerging Infectious Diseases. In: NIH Education, Understanding Infectious Diseases. Available at http://science.education.nih.gov/supplements/nih1/diseases/guide/understanding1.htm Accessed 1/4/2012.

Health-care Associated Infections. http://www.cdc.gov/hai/

Infectious Disease Organisms. In: Global RPh - Drugs of choice. Antibiotic choices. Empiric therapy. Available at http://www.globalrph.com. Accessed 2/29/2012.

Infectious Diseases Society of America Standards, Practice Guidelines, and Statements. In: Infectious Diseases Society of America (IDSA). Available at www.idsociety.org/Content.aspx?id=9088. Accessed 2/19/2012.

Micromedex Healthcare Series. www.micromedex.com/products/hcs/

SHEA Guidelines and Resources. Compendium of Strategies to Prevent HAIs. Available at http://www.shea-online.org/GuidelinesResources/CompendiumofStrategiestoPreventHAIs.aspx

Surbhi L, Terrell CL, Edson RS. General Principles of Antimicrobial Therapy. In: Mayo Clinic Proceedings from the Department of Epidemiology, University of Maryland, Baltimore (S.L.); and Division of Infectious Diseases, Mayo Clinic, Rochester, MN (C.L.T., R.S.E.). 2011. Available at www.mayoclinicproceedings.com. Accessed 1/17/2012.

Teflaro. http://www.teflaro.com/

The Sanford Guide to Antimicrobial Therapy 41st edition, 2011. http://www.sanfordguide.com

World Health Organization. http://www.who.int

Appendix A

Quick Facts: Methicillin Resistant *Staphylococcus Aureus* (MRSA)

- MRSA is an aerobic or facultative anaerobic, coagulase-positive organism. It can survive in the presence or absence of atmospheric oxygen.
- MRSA presents a serious threat to patient health and safety across practice settings as well as in the community.
- MRSA is addressed in the US Department of Health and Human Services HAI Action Plan. The plan identifies the targets and metrics for national prevention efforts in the US.
- According to studies conducted by the CDC and other researchers, MRSA infections in patients in US hospitals, including those with MRSA bloodstream infections, are declining.
- MRSA in the community most often presents as skin infections. The incidence of community acquired MRSA does not appear to be decreasing based on the available public health data.
- MRSA colonization (no sign of active infection) appears to be increasing. The extent to which the increase is attributable to much wider adoption of active surveillance testing (screening in the absence of symptoms of infection) is unknown. The impact of public reporting on increased rates of colonization has not yet been fully explored.
- Decolonization of the nares using mupirocin ointment often yields only transient improvement.
- MRSA colonization increases the probability that the patient will eventually an active MRSA infection.
- Contact precautions are implemented for patients colonized with MRSA and those with active MRSA infections. Institutional polices regarding the discontinuation of contact precautions vary widely and are often based on obtaining negative cultures from multiple body sites during a specified period of time.
- The most commonly obtained MRSA cultures are from skin/wounds, blood, urine and sputum.
- When obtaining a MRSA culture from a wound, clean the infected site of drainage using a sterile irrigant (sterile saline is often used). An accurate culture can only be obtained if old organic matter and accumulated wound drainage have first been removed.

- When obtaining MRSA cultures from indwelling devices (e.g. vascular access or urinary catheters) follow the institution's instructions to reduce the potential contamination of the specimen by exposure to bacterial biofilm.
- Patient bathing (actively by self or passively by a caregiver) with a chlorhexidine gluconate product reduces the MRSA bioburden on skin and may be a useful adjunct to prevention efforts in designated situations.

References

Methicillin resistant Staphylococcus aureus (MRSA) infections. CDC website 2012. Available at http://www.cdc.gov/mrsa. Accessed April 2, 2012.

Precautions to prevent the spread of MRSA in healthcare settings. CDC website 2012. Available at http://www.cdc.gov/mrsa/prevent/healthcare/precautions.html. Accessed April 2, 2012.

Appendix B

Quick Facts: *Clostridium difficile* (C. diff)

- Clostridium difficile is a spore-forming, gram-positive anaerobic bacillus that produces two exotoxins: toxin A and toxin B.
- Symptoms of CDI include diarrhea, fever, nausea and poor appetite, and abdominal pain or tenderness.
- Clostridium difficile infection (CDI), once primarily associated with healthcare settings, is increasingly common in the community.
- CDI is addressed in the US Department of Health and Human Services HAI Action Plan. The plan identifies the targets and metrics for national prevention efforts in the US.
- According to studies conducted by the CDC and other researchers, CDI rates are at an historic high in the United States.
- Exposure to antibiotics is a leading cause of CDI. In approximately 20% of patients, CDI will resolve within 2–3 days after antibiotics are withdrawn.
- CDI can lead to serious complications and result in high mortality rates among patients who are elderly, have serious underlying health conditions, are immunocompromised, and have long periods of hospitalization.
- Patients with CDI are placed on contact precautions. Because patients continue shed spores after the cessation of diarrhea, contact precautions are usually continued for several additional days following clinical improvement.
- Hand hygiene is done with soap and water. Alcohol based hand rubs are far less effective and are not recommended.
- Rigorous environmental cleaning and surface disinfection are required to control the spread of CDI. Standard EPA disinfectants should not be used; EPA registered sporicidal disinfectants are necessary. Alternately, solutions of hypochlorite (household bleach) are highly effective but may be too harsh for some institutional surfaces. Monitor the correct use of approved disinfectants per manufacturer's directions and institutional policies and procedures.
- Since 2000 a new highly virulent epidemic strain of CDI has emerged and is seen in younger patients traditionally thought to be at much lower risk. The epidemic strain may be referred to as type BI, North American Pulsed Field type 1 (NAP1), or PCR ribotype 027. In addition to its toxin production, this new strain is often resistant to fluoroquinolones.

- CDI diagnostic testing may include molecular, antigen and/or toxin testing. Stool cultures, although highly sensitive, are done less frequently than in the past, due to the frequency of false positive results and the delayed turnaround time. Verify with the laboratory which testing methods are used and the expected turnaround time for results.

References

Clostridium difficile infection. CDC web site 201. Available at http://www.cdc.gov/HAI/organisms/cdiff/Cdiff_infect.html, Accessed April 6, 2012.

Gould CV, McDonald LC. Bench-to-beside review: Clostridium difficile colitis. *Crit Care* 2008;12(1):203. Epub 2008 Jan 18.

Appendix C

Quick Facts: Seasonal Influenza (Flu)

- Seasonal flu is a respiratory illness caused by influenza viruses. Types A and B are the most common causes of seasonal flu epidemics. Specific types of flu (e.g., swine, bat, bird etc.) are reported separately and not included in seasonal influenza programs.
- "Flu season" is generally associated with fall and winter months, but can peak in late spring. The CDC conducts year round influenza surveillance to carefully monitor strains, prevalence, regional variations and severity, especially in high risk groups.
- Influenza is spread primarily person-to-person through large particle respiratory droplet transmission. Contact with contaminated surfaces and airborne transmissions are also possible but thought not to be as common as droplet transmission and are not as well documented in scientific studies at this time.
- Symptoms of the flu may be difficult to differentiate from other respiratory illness. Flu symptoms include fever, chills, cough, sore throat, headache, rhinitis, myalgia, and fatigue. Vomiting and diarrhea have also been reported.
- Influenza prevention is based on annual vaccination. All persons aged 6 months and older should be vaccinated unless specific medical contraindications exist. For example, individuals with a febrile or other serious illness should delay vaccination until directed by their physician. Vaccination is usually not recommended for individuals who have a serious allergy to any vaccine component (most often eggs).
- If vaccines are in short supply, the CDC provides risk criteria to direct limited quantities to those most susceptible and/or at risk for serious complications. See the CDC web site for the Summary of Influenza Recommendations.
- There are two major types of flu vaccine available: TIV (trivalent influenza vaccine) administered as an intramuscular injection (the traditional "flu shot") and LAIV (live attenuated influenza vaccine) administered as a nasal spray. An intradermal preparation is also available.
- Following immunization programs, hand hygiene, respiratory etiquette, use of face masks, tissue to contain secretions and reducing exposure to infected individuals are the mainstays of infection prevention programs.
- Two classes of drugs are currently available for treatment of seasonal influenza: neuraminidase inhibitors are effective against both types A and

B. Adamantanes, used to treat Type A, are no longer recommended due to increasing levels of resistance.

- A variety of diagnostic tests are available for influenza but their availability differs among laboratories. It is important to know which tests are readily available and their specific specimen collection requirements.
- Rapid influenza diagnostic tests (RIDT) provide results in less than 30 minutes. Commercially available RIDTs differ in their diagnostic uses; some only detect Type A. RIDT is less sensitive than viral culture or RT-PCR in detecting seasonal influenza Type A.

References

Seasonal influenza (flu). CDC web site 2-012. Available at http://www.cdc.gov/flu Accessed April 5, 2012.

Appendix D

Quick Facts: Antibiograms

An antibiogram is a table that allows healthcare personnel to see information about the pathogens most commonly found in the hospital and the antimicrobials to which those pathogens are susceptible. In the example on page 83, oxacillin <u>resistant</u> *S. aureus* accounted for 59% of all the *S. aureus* found (oxacillin <u>sensitive</u> *S. aureus* – the line below – accounted for the rest.) None of the, oxacillin resistant *S. aureus* was sensitive to oxacillin, but 100 percent was sensitive to vancomycin. Each box in the grid indicates what percentage of the organisms were sensitive to a particular antimicrobial.

- Antibiograms are generally prepared by the laboratory according to the Clinical Laboratory Standards Institute (CLSI) guidelines (document M39-A2).
- Data is analyzed for the most common isolates (usually 30) for a given pathogen.
- Antibiograms report susceptibility only to antimicrobials that are routinely used.
- Antibiograms help to answer two questions:
  - For this pathogen in this hospital, what is the best antimicrobial to use? (Highest susceptibility)
  - Has the susceptibility of this pathogen changed or increased?
- Only the first isolate is included for patients with multiple positive cultures. If there are multiple positive cultures, or multiple organisms suspected, the microbiology laboratory is the place to go for additional information.
- Antibiograms report the percentage of susceptible isolates. This does not include the isolates with intermediate susceptibility. (The exception is intermediate susceptibility of *S. pneumoniae* to penicillin.)
- Changing resistance may indicate a need for increased infection prevention interventions.

References

Arnold F. Antimicrobials and Resistance. In: Grota P, ed. *APIC Text of Infection Control and Epidemiology*, 4th ed. Washington, DC: Association for Professionals in Infection Control and Epidemiology, 2014.

Clinical and Laboratory Standards Institute. Analysis and Presentation of Cumulative Antimicrobial Susceptibility Test Data: Approved Guideline, 2nd ed. CLSI document M39-A2. Reston, VA: Clinical and Laboratory Standards Institute; 2005.

Annual Antimicrobic Susceptibility Report for 20X. (Data analysis based on first isolate per patient per year.)

Percent Susceptible

Organism	Number of Isolates Tested	Penicillin	Ceftriaxone (Susceptible)	Oxacillin	Erythromycin	Clindamycin	Vancomycin	TMP/SMZ	Ampicillin	Ampicillin/Sulbactam	Cefazolin	Cefepime	Ceftriaxone	Gentamicin	Gentamicin (High dose)	Tobramycin	Levofloxacin	Ciprofloxacin	Aztreonam	Imipenem	Piperacillin/Tazobactam	Amikacin	Nitrofurantion (Urine)	Amoxicillin/Clav. Acid (Urine)
Gram positive																								
S. aureus - oxacillin resistant	1149/1926 (59%)			0	5	66	100	98															99	
S. aureus - oxacillin sensitive	777/1926 (41%)			100	60	85	100	99															99	
coagulase negative Staph (CNS)	192			31	22	47	100	64															99	
Enterococcus faecium	29						28		14						100								54	
Enterococcus faecalis	95						79		93						47								100	
Gram negative																								
Enterobacter spp - non-urine	150							91		35		95	81	95		87		82	77		81			
Enterobacter spp - urine	197							82				96	83	95				79					71	
Klebsiella spp - non-urine	193							88		63	72	95	84	98		96		90	83		85	100		
Klebsiella spp - urine	682							89		58	78	96	94	98				91					85	89
Escherichia coli - non-urine	301							83	54	58	87	99	95	93		94		81	96		98	100		
Escherichia coli - urine	3359							83	60		94	100	99	95				88					98	87

From: Sykora C. Antimicrobial Testing. In: Kulich PA and Taylor DL. *The Infection Preventionist's Guide to the Lab.* Washington, DC: Association for Professionals in Infection Control and Epidemiology, 2012.

Appendix E

Quick Facts: Contact Precautions

- Contact precautions are used to reduce the risk of contamination and transmission of pathogenic microorganisms spread by direct or indirect contact with the patient and/or the patient's environment.
- Contact Precautions are one of three types of Transmission Based Precautions. The other two types are Droplet Precautions and Airborne Precautions.
- Contact precautions are most used in healthcare settings to prevent the transmission of MRSA and *Clostridium difficile*. However, Contact Precautions may be used for other microorganisms as well.
- Contact Precautions are used in addition to Standard Precautions.
- In acute care, patients who require Contact Precautions should be placed in a private room. If a private room is not available, patient cohorting should be implemented.
- In non acute settings, including ambulatory care, patient placement should be expedited and carefully managed to reduce the risk of transmission to other patients.
- Gowns and gloves must be removed when exiting the patient's room (or other area of placement). When the gown and gloves have been discarded, hand hygiene is performed as the final step and before the healthcare worker moves on to his or her next task.
- Lab coats, scrub attire and personal garments (e.g. sweaters, jackets) are not used in lieu of institutionally provided gowns for contact precautions.
- Gowns may not be worn outside their designated area for use (e.g. patient room, cubicle, treatment room) and are not reused.
- To the extent possible, dedicated equipment should be used for patients requiring Contact Precautions. Disposable, noncritical equipment should also be considered. If these options are not feasible, equipment must be thoroughly cleaned and disinfected before use by another patient. Equipment taken to a reprocessing/soiled utility area should be placed in a plastic bag for transport.
- Spaces occupied by patients on Contact Precautions should be cleaned at least daily with emphasis on high touch surfaces such as bed rails, table tops, door handles, and bathroom fixtures.

- Contact Precautions are required even if the healthcare worker or visitor has no direct contact with the patient. The high levels of environmental microbial contamination and the persistence of microbes on high touch surfaces support the rigorous use of Contact Precautions by all who enter the room.

References

Siegel J, Rhinehart E, Jackson M, Chiarello L, the Healthcare Infection Control Practices Advisory Committee. Guideline for Isolation Precautions: Preventing Transmission of Infectious Agents in Healthcare Settings. CDC. 2007. Available at: http://www.cdc.gov/hicpac/2007IP/2007isolationPrecau tions.html

Appendix F

Quick Facts: Common Pathogens by Site

Type of Infection	Common Pathogens
Skin, subcutaneous tissue	*Staphylococcus aureus, Streptococcus pyogenes, Candida,* dermatophytes, coagulase-negative *Staphylococcus, Pseudomonas, Clostridium*
Sinusitis	*Streptococcus pneumoniae, Haemophilus influenzae, S. pyogenes, S. aureus,* gram-negative bacilli, *Mucorales*
Pharyngitis	Respiratory viruses, *S. pyogenes, Candida albicans, Neisseria gonorrhoeae, Corynebacterium diphtheriae*
Bronchitis	Respiratory viruses (especially respiratory syncytial virus [RSV]) among pediatrics), *S. pneumoniae, H. influenzae, Bordetella pertussis*
Pneumonia (community acquired)	Respiratory viruses (e.g., influenza, RSV, hantavirus), *S. pneumoniae, H. influenzae, Mycoplasma pneumoniae, Chlamydia pneumoniae, Mycobacterium tuberculosis, S. aureus,* gram-negative bacilli, *Legionella pneumophila, Pneumocystis carinii*
Empyema	*Anaerobes,* oral streptococci, *S. aureus, S. pyogenes, H. influenzae*
Nosocomial pneumonia	*Pseudomonas,* Enterobacteriaceae, *S. aureus, Legionella, S. pneumoniae*
Endocarditis	*Streptococcus viridans, S. aureus, Enterococcus, Haemophilus, Staphylococcus epidermidis, Candida*
Gastroenteritis	*Salmonella, Shigella, Campylobacter,* invasive *Escherichia coli,* viruses, *Giardia, Yersinia, Vibrio*
Peritonitis, abdominal	*Bacteroides,* anaerobic cocci, Enterobacteriaceae, *Enterococcus,* abscess *S. aureus, Candida*
Urinary tract infection	*E. coli, Klebsiella, Proteus, Enterococcus, Pseudomonas, Staphylococcus saprophyticus, Candida*
Pelvic inflammatory	*Chlamydia trachomatis, Gonococcus, Bacteroides,* Enterobacteriaceae disease
Osteomyelitis	*S. aureus, Salmonella, Pseudomonas, Staphylococcus. Agalactiae*
Septic arthritis	*S. aureus, N. gonorrhoeae, S. pneumoniae, S. pyogenes, Pasteurella multocida*
Meningitis	*H. influenzae, Neisseria meningitidis, S. pneumoniae, S. agalactiae, M. tuberculosis*
Septicemia	*S. aureus, S. pneumoniae, E. coli, Klebsiella, Salmonella, Candida, Clostridium, Listeria*
Device-associated infections	Coagulase-negative *Staphylococcus, Corynebacterium,* gram-negative *bacilli, infection Candida,* or any organism listed under septicemia

(Source: *APIC Text of Infection Control and Epidemiology,* 2009.)

Appendix G

Quick Facts: Antimicrobial Stewardship

- The misuse and overuse of antimicrobials is considered one of the world's most pressing public health problems.
- Despite prevention strategies, the proportion of resistant strains causing health care and community associated infections continues to increase while the number of new antimicrobials continues to decrease.
- The CDC's awareness and education site about antibiotic use *Get Smart About Healthcare* is available at www.cdc.gov/getsmart/healthcare
- Interventions and programs designed to improve antibiotic use are referred to as antimicrobial stewardship (AS) and antimicrobial stewardship programs (ASP).
- ASP requires an inter-professional, integrated team based approach for maximum impact across the continuum of care.
- AS teams are led by a physician and a pharmacist. Healthcare epidemiologists and infection preventionists are also key members of the AS team.
- To reduce antibiotic overutilization, clinicians should check that all antibiotic orders are accompanied by a dose, duration and indication. This helps clinicians change or stop therapy when appropriate.
- Assure that antibiotic use is tailored to the susceptibility results performed with culturing.
- Take an "antibiotic timeout" when culture results are available, usually within 48 hours. Use this time to ask if the antibiotic is still warranted or if the antibiotic still effective against the identified organism(s).
- Standard and transmission based precautions are used to help manage the transmission of pathogens, including multi drug resistant organisms.

References

Moody J, Cosgrove S, Olmsted R, Septimus E, Aureden K, Oriola S, et al. Antimicrobial stewardship; a collaborative partnership between infection preventionists and health care epidemiologists. *Am J Infect Control* 2012 Mar; 40(2):94-95.

Get Smart About Healthcare. CDC website site 2012; available at http://www.cdc.gov/getsmart/healthcare; accessed April 12, 2012.

Index